# EVERY DAY COUNTS®

# PRACTICE COUNTS

Gillespie • Kanter • Clark

## GRADE 2

GREAT SOURCE®
A Division of Houghton Mifflin Company

**Credits**

Cover Illustration: Amy Vangsgaurd
Layout Production: PC&F, Inc. and Taurins Design



Printed in the United States of America



International Standard Book Number: 978-0-669-00882-1

9 10 11 12 13 0304 22 21 20 19 18

4500701137

www.greatsource.com

# DAY 1 — AUG./SEPT.

**Add.**

1. 

   ____ + ____ = ____

2. 

   ____ + ____ = ____

3. 

   ____ + ____ = ____

4. 

   ____ + ____ = ____

**Continue the pattern.**

5. △ □ △ □ ____ ____ ____ □

6. A B A B ____ ____ ____ B

# DAY 2

**Add.**

1. 

   ____ + ____ = ____

2. 

   ____ + ____ = ____

3. 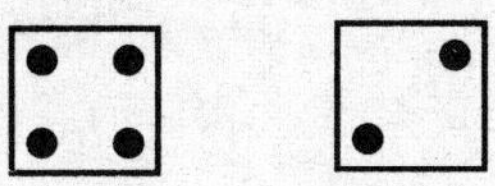

   ____ + ____ = ____

4. 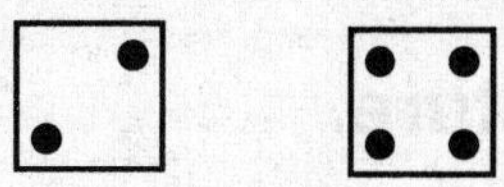

   ____ + ____ = ____

**Write how much.**

5.  = ______¢

# DAY 3

**Add.**

**1.** 2 + 1 = ______ **2.** 3 + 2 = ______ **3.** 1 + 2 = ______

**4.** 1 + 4 = ______ **5.** 3 + 3 = ______ **6.** 5 + 1 = ______

**Color the shapes.**

**7.** △ Blue

○ Red

▭ Green

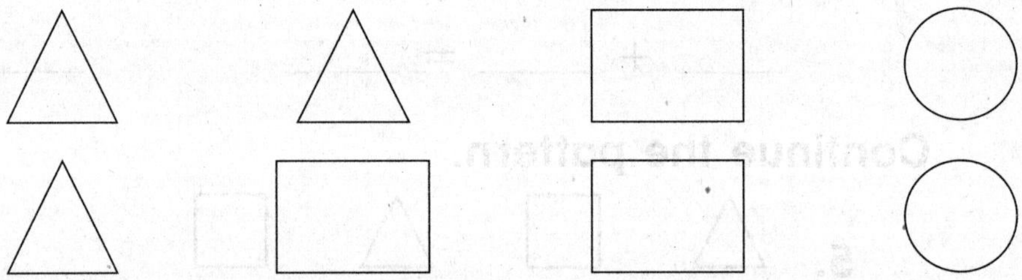

# DAY 4

**Add.**

**1.** 1 + 1 = ______ **2.** 2 + 1 = ______ **3.** 3 + 1 = ______

**4.** 4 + 1 = ______ **5.** 5 + 1 = ______

**Solve.**
**Draw the picture.**

**6.** There were 2 black cats in a tree.
There were 3 yellow cats in the tree.
How many cats were in the tree? ______ cats

# DAY 5

**Add.**

1. 4 + 2 = ______ **2.** 2 + 4 = ______ **3.** 5 + 1 = ______

4. 1 + 5 = ______ **5.** 3 + 2 = ______ **6.** 2 + 3 = ______

**Choose a number sentence.**
**Draw a picture of it.**

7.

# DAY 6

**Add.**
**Use the Counting Tape.**
**Count on.**

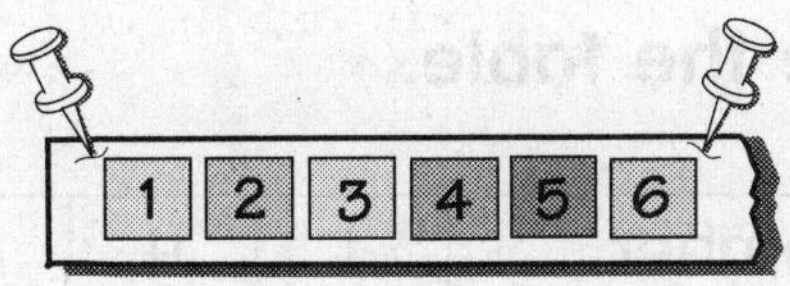


1. 4 + ______ = 6 **2.** 3 + ______ = 6 **3.** 5 + ______ = 6

4. 4 + ______ = 5 **5.** 3 + ______ = 5 **6.** 2 + ______ = 5

**Complete the patterns.**

7. 1, 2, 3, ___, ___, ___ **8.** 11, 12, 13, ___, ___, ___

9. 5, 10, 15, ___, ___, ___ **10.** 2, 4, 6, ___, ___, ___

# DAY 7

Add.
Use the Counting Tape.
Count on.

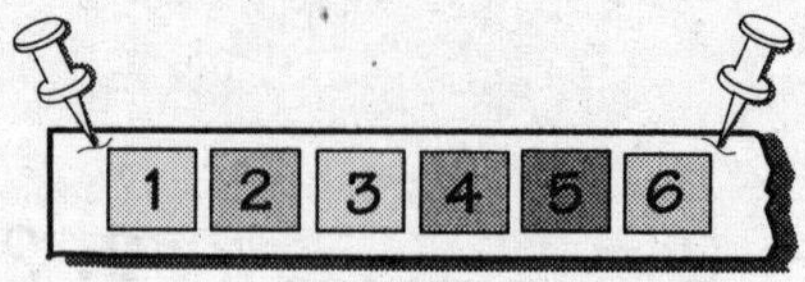


1. 2 + ______ = 3

2. 2 + ______ = 4

3. 2 + ______ = 5

4. 4 + ______ = 6

Use the shapes.
Draw a picture.

5. 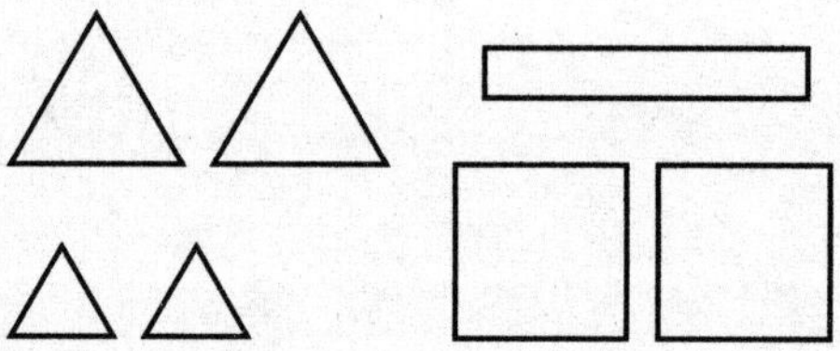

# DAY 8

Complete the table.

1.

| Number | 1 | 4 | 5 | 3 | 2 |
|---|---|---|---|---|---|
| 1 more | | | | | |

2.

| Number | 2 | 1 | 3 | 4 |
|---|---|---|---|---|
| 2 more | | | | |

Count the money. Circle which is more.

3.  __5__ ¢  __6__ ¢

# DAY 9

**Add.**

**1.** 5 + 1 = ______ **2.** 2 + 4 = ______ **3.** 3 + 1 = ______

**Solve.**

**4.** Maria made 3 pictures on Monday.
She made 2 pictures on Tuesday.
How many pictures did she make? ______ pictures

# DAY 10 CHECKPOINT

**Add.**

**1.** 5 + 1 = ______ **2.** 3 + 2 = ______ **3.** 2 + 2 = ______

**Complete the patterns.**

**4.** 5, 10, 15, ______, ______, ______

**5.** 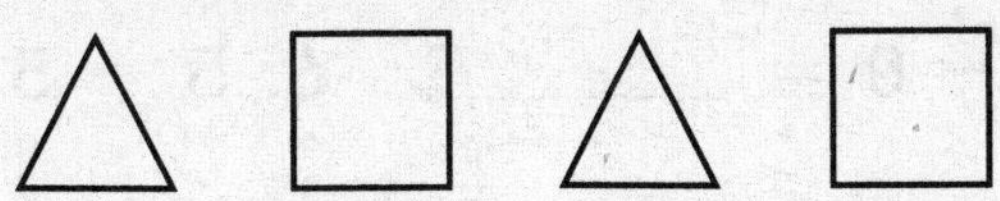 ______ ______ ______ ______

**Write how much.**

**6.**

______¢

**7.**

______¢

# DAY 11

**Subtract.**
**Use counters.**

1. 6 − 1 = ______ **2.** 5 − 1 = ______ **3.** 4 − 1 = ______

4. 3 − 1 = ______ **5.** 2 − 1 = ______ **6.** 1 − 1 = ______

**Complete the pattern.**

**7.** 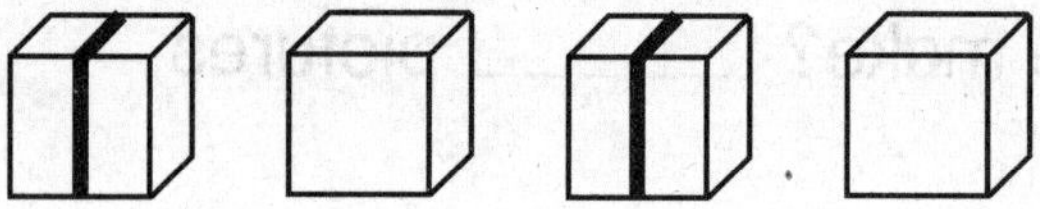 ____ ____ ____ ____

**8.** A B A B ____ ____ ____ ____

# DAY 12

**Subtract.**
**Use counters.**

1. 5 − 4 = ______ **2.** 5 − 3 = ______ **3.** 5 − 2 = ______

4. 5 − 1 = ______ **5.** 5 − 0 = ______ **6.** 5 − 5 = ______

**Count the money. Circle which is more.**

**7.**

______¢

______¢

**8.**

______¢

______¢

# DAY 13

**Make a fact.**

**Write the number sentence.**

1. 

_____ – _____ = _____

2. 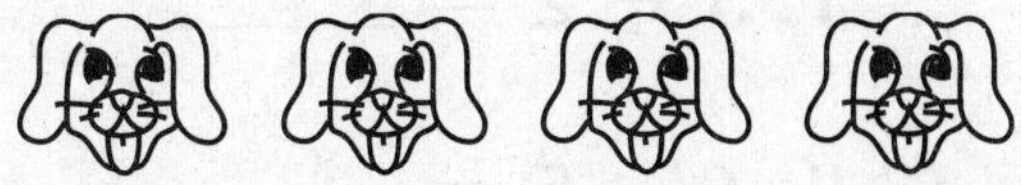

_____ – _____ = _____

3. 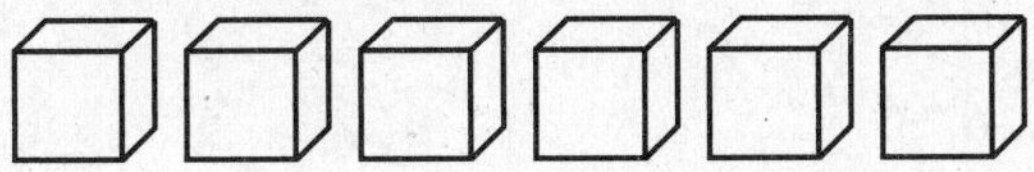

_____ – _____ = _____

4. 

_____ – _____ = _____

**Draw three things that are rectangles.**

5.

**Draw two things that are circles.**

6.

# DAY 14

**Subtract.**

1. $\begin{array}{r} 6 \\ -3 \\ \hline \end{array}$

2. $\begin{array}{r} 3 \\ -1 \\ \hline \end{array}$

3. $\begin{array}{r} 4 \\ -2 \\ \hline \end{array}$

4. $\begin{array}{r} 6 \\ -5 \\ \hline \end{array}$

5. $\begin{array}{r} 2 \\ -1 \\ \hline \end{array}$

6. $\begin{array}{r} 5 \\ -3 \\ \hline \end{array}$

7. $\begin{array}{r} 6 \\ -4 \\ \hline \end{array}$

8. $\begin{array}{r} 6 \\ -2 \\ \hline \end{array}$

**Solve.**

9. Bart has 6 cats. He has 4 dogs.
How many more cats than dogs? _____ more cats
How did you solve the problem? __________________

# DAY 15

**Subtract.**

**1.** 3 − 2 = ______ **2.** 5 − 4 = ______ **3.** 4 − 3 = ______

**4.** 6 − 5 = ______ **5.** 6 − 3 = ______ **6.** 2 − 1 = ______

**Use the Calendar.**
**Count back to solve.**

**7.** Today is September ________.

**8.** 3 days ago was September ________.

______ − 3 = ______

# DAY 16

**Subtract.**

**1.** $\begin{array}{r} 6 \\ -4 \\ \hline \end{array}$ **2.** $\begin{array}{r} 6 \\ -2 \\ \hline \end{array}$ **3.** $\begin{array}{r} 5 \\ -4 \\ \hline \end{array}$ **4.** $\begin{array}{r} 5 \\ -1 \\ \hline \end{array}$

**5.** $\begin{array}{r} 4 \\ -3 \\ \hline \end{array}$ **6.** $\begin{array}{r} 4 \\ -1 \\ \hline \end{array}$ **7.** $\begin{array}{r} 6 \\ -5 \\ \hline \end{array}$ **8.** $\begin{array}{r} 6 \\ -1 \\ \hline \end{array}$

**Make the fact family.**

**9.** 1 + 4 = ______ 5 − 1 = ______

______ + ______ = ______ 5 − ______ = ______

**Complete the pattern. Label it.**

**10.** ○ △ ○ △ ____ ____ ____ ____

# DAY 17

**Add.**

**1.** 3 + 2 = ______ **2.** 4 + 1 = ______ **3.** 2 + 4 = ______

**Subtract.**

**4.** 5 − 3 = ______ **5.** 4 − 1 = ______ **6.** 6 − 4 = ______

**Count the money. Circle which is more.**
**Write how much.**

**7.**

______¢

**8.**

______¢

# DAY 18

**Write the fact families.**

**1.** __4__ + __2__ = __6__

______ + ______ = ______

__6__ − ______ = ______

______ − ______ = ______

**2.** __2__ + __3__ = __5__

______ + ______ = ______

______ − ______ = ______

______ − ______ = ______

**Circle the number in the ones place.**

**3.** 73 **4.** 24 **5.** 9 **6.** 14

**7.** 35 **8.** 8 **9.** 46 **10.** 17

# DAY 19

**Add or subtract.**

1. $\begin{array}{r} 5 \\ -2 \\ \hline \end{array}$ 2. $\begin{array}{r} 6 \\ -4 \\ \hline \end{array}$ 3. $\begin{array}{r} 4 \\ +1 \\ \hline \end{array}$ 4. $\begin{array}{r} 1 \\ +5 \\ \hline \end{array}$

5. $\begin{array}{r} 3 \\ -2 \\ \hline \end{array}$ 6. $\begin{array}{r} 4 \\ -3 \\ \hline \end{array}$ 7. $\begin{array}{r} 6 \\ -5 \\ \hline \end{array}$ 8. $\begin{array}{r} 3 \\ +2 \\ \hline \end{array}$

**Look at the Calendar.**

9. How many days are in September? ______

10. How many Mondays? ______

# DAY 20

**Add or subtract.**

1. $\begin{array}{r} 6 \\ -3 \\ \hline \end{array}$ 2. $\begin{array}{r} 2 \\ +3 \\ \hline \end{array}$ 3. $\begin{array}{r} 5 \\ -4 \\ \hline \end{array}$ 4. $\begin{array}{r} 5 \\ -1 \\ \hline \end{array}$

5. $\begin{array}{r} 3 \\ -2 \\ \hline \end{array}$ 6. $\begin{array}{r} 4 \\ -3 \\ \hline \end{array}$ 7. $\begin{array}{r} 6 \\ -5 \\ \hline \end{array}$ 8. $\begin{array}{r} 3 \\ +2 \\ \hline \end{array}$

**Solve.**

9. Ryan's aunt is coming on Tuesday, September 2.
She will stay 5 days.
What will the date be when she leaves? ______________________
How did you find out? ______________________

______________________

# Monthly Assessment

**Use the Calendar.**

1. Write the name of this month.

_______________

2. What date is the second Monday?

_______________

3. What day is September 20? _______________

4. What is the pattern? _______________

_______________

_______________

5. Which days have squares? _______________

_______________

6. Are all the shapes rectangles? Why? _______________

_______________

**Complete the pattern.**

7. 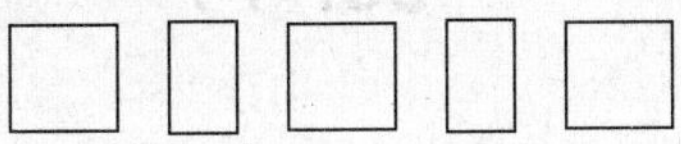 ___ What is the next shape? Why?

_______________

8. 2, 4, 6, ______, ______, ______, ______, ______

What do you notice about this pattern? _______________

_______________

# Monthly Assessment

**Add.**

**Circle the fact pairs.**

| | | | | | |
|---|---|---|---|---|---|
| **1.** $\begin{array}{r} 4 \\ +2 \\ \hline \end{array}$ | **2.** $\begin{array}{r} 6 \\ +0 \\ \hline \end{array}$ | **3.** $\begin{array}{r} 3 \\ +1 \\ \hline \end{array}$ | **4.** $\begin{array}{r} 2 \\ +3 \\ \hline \end{array}$ | **5.** $\begin{array}{r} 5 \\ +1 \\ \hline \end{array}$ | **6.** $\begin{array}{r} 3 \\ +3 \\ \hline \end{array}$ |
| **7.** $\begin{array}{r} 0 \\ +6 \\ \hline \end{array}$ | **8.** $\begin{array}{r} 1 \\ +3 \\ \hline \end{array}$ | **9.** $\begin{array}{r} 2 \\ +4 \\ \hline \end{array}$ | **10.** $\begin{array}{r} 1 \\ +5 \\ \hline \end{array}$ | **11.** $\begin{array}{r} 3 \\ +2 \\ \hline \end{array}$ | **12.** $\begin{array}{r} 3 \\ +0 \\ \hline \end{array}$ |

**Subtract.**

| | | | | | | |
|---|---|---|---|---|---|---|
| **13.** $\begin{array}{r} 6 \\ -2 \\ \hline \end{array}$ | **14.** $\begin{array}{r} 5 \\ -3 \\ \hline \end{array}$ | **15.** $\begin{array}{r} 4 \\ -3 \\ \hline \end{array}$ | **16.** $\begin{array}{r} 2 \\ -2 \\ \hline \end{array}$ | **17.** $\begin{array}{r} 6 \\ -5 \\ \hline \end{array}$ | **18.** $\begin{array}{r} 3 \\ -1 \\ \hline \end{array}$ | **19.** $\begin{array}{r} 4 \\ -2 \\ \hline \end{array}$ |
| **20.** $\begin{array}{r} 6 \\ -6 \\ \hline \end{array}$ | **21.** $\begin{array}{r} 5 \\ -4 \\ \hline \end{array}$ | **22.** $\begin{array}{r} 4 \\ -1 \\ \hline \end{array}$ | **23.** $\begin{array}{r} 2 \\ -0 \\ \hline \end{array}$ | **24.** $\begin{array}{r} 5 \\ -1 \\ \hline \end{array}$ | **25.** $\begin{array}{r} 4 \\ -0 \\ \hline \end{array}$ | **26.** $\begin{array}{r} 2 \\ -1 \\ \hline \end{array}$ |

**Circle the number in the ones place.**

**27.** 62 **28.** 34 **29.** 18 **30.** 79 **31.** 63

**32.** Your friend says that he can have 12 in the ones place.

Do you agree? ______

Explain. ______________________________

______________________________

# MONTHLY ASSESSMENT

**Solve.**

1. Randy had 6 puppies. He gave 4 away.
   How many does he have left? ______
   How did you find your answer?

2. Dominika built 1 house with blocks.
   Then she built 4 more houses with boxes.
   How many houses did she build?
   ______ houses

   Show your work.

3. Tom needs 6 stickers for his toy truck.
   He put on 2 stickers. How many more stickers will he put on? ______ stickers

   Show how you solved it.

**Draw a picture and solve.**

4. Wong ate 2 pretzels.
   Then he ate 3 more pretzels.
   How many pretzels did Wong eat? ______

# Monthly Assessment

**Draw something you see in the room.**

**1.** square | circle | rectangle

**Write how much.**

**2.**

______¢

**3.**

______¢

**4.**

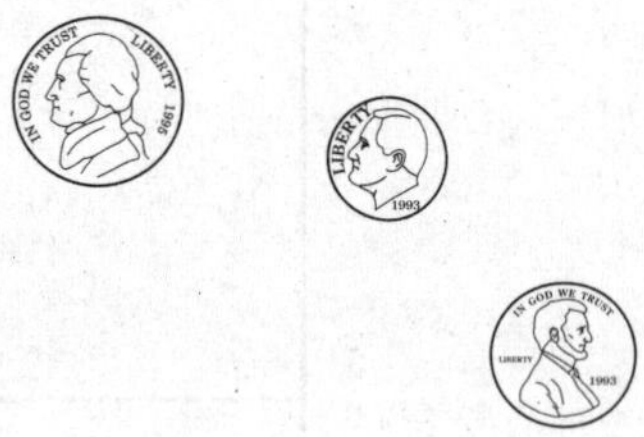

______¢

**5.**

______¢

**Solve.**

**6.** Jordan has 6 nickels. Kyle has 6 pennies. They both have 6 coins.
Who has more money? ______________
Explain. ______________________________________________

# DAY 1 — OCTOBER

**Show ways to make 7.**

1. ______ + ______ = 7 2. ______ + ______ = 7

3. ______ + ______ = 7 4. ______ + ______ = 7

**Continue each pattern.**

5. ○ ○ ○ ● ○ ○ ○ ● ○ ___ ___ ___ ___ ___

6. | — — | — — | — — ___ ___ ___

7. 2, 4, 6, 8, 10, ______, ______, ______, ______, ______

# DAY 2

**Add.**

1. 4 + 0 = ______ 2. 0 + 9 = ______ 3. 15 + 0 = ______

4. When I add 0 to a number, ______________________________

______________________________________________

**Answer the questions.**

5. On what day of school will the Coin Counter have 2 dimes, 1 nickel, and 4 pennies? ______________

6. Tell or show how you got your answer. ______________

______________________________________________

______________________________________________

# Day 3

**Add.**

1. 4 + 5 = ______ 2. 5 + 5 = ______ 3. 5 + 6 = ______

4. 5 + 3 = ______ 5. 15 + 3 = ______ 6. 35 + 3 = ______

**Circle the 2 shapes that are the same.**

7. 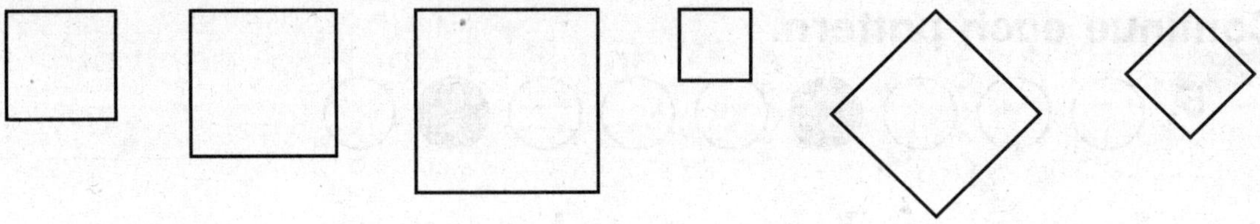

# Day 4

**Add.**

1. 8 + 2 = ______ 2. 18 + 2 = ______ 3. 28 + 2 = ______

4. 2 + 7 = ______ 5. 2 + 17 = ______ 6. 2 + 27 = ______

7. When I add 2 to a number, ________________________________

________________________________________________

**Look at the graph. Answer the questions.**

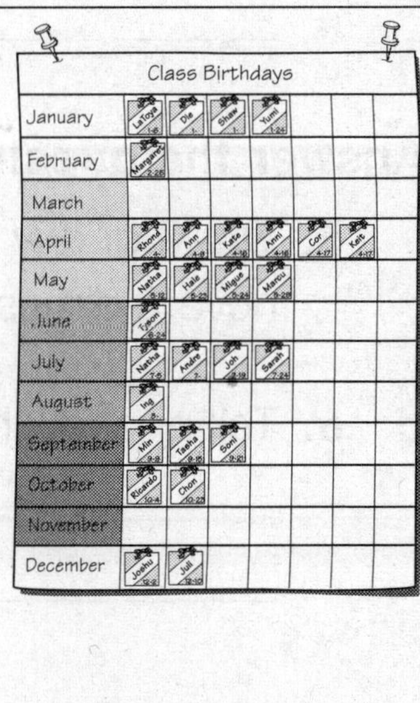


8. How many fewer birthdays are in October than September? ______

9. How many more birthdays are in September than August? ______

# DAY 5

Add.

1. 1 + 12 = ______  2. 23 + 1 = ______  3. 1 + 34 = ______

Subtract.

4. 99 − 1 = ______  5. 78 − 1 = ______  6. 14 − 1 = ______

Use 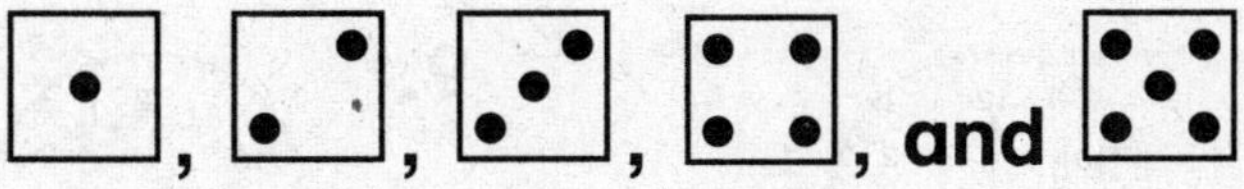 , and , to make each sum.

7. 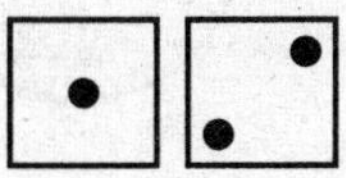

1 + 2 = 3

8. ______ + ______ = 5

9. ______ + ______ = 7

# DAY 6

Show ways to make 8.

1. ______ + ______ = 8  2. ______ + ______ = 8

3. ______ + ______ = 8  4. ______ + ______ = 8

5. ______ + ______ = 8  6. ______ + ______ = 8

Continue the pattern.

7.  ______

1  3  5  7  ______

# DAY 7

**Add.**

1. 7 + 1 = ______
2. 17 + 1 = ______
3. 27 + 1 = ______
4. 5 + 2 = ______
5. 15 + 2 = ______
6. 25 + 2 = ______

**Write the time.**

7. 

☐:☐☐

8. 

☐:☐☐

9. 

☐:☐☐

# DAY 8

**Add.**

1. $\begin{array}{r} 4 \\ +\ 3 \\ \hline \end{array}$
2. $\begin{array}{r} 3 \\ +\ 4 \\ \hline \end{array}$
3. $\begin{array}{r} 4 \\ +\ 4 \\ \hline \end{array}$
4. $\begin{array}{r} 8 \\ +\ 0 \\ \hline \end{array}$

**Subtract.**

5. $\begin{array}{r} 7 \\ -\ 1 \\ \hline \end{array}$
6. $\begin{array}{r} 47 \\ -\ 1 \\ \hline \end{array}$
7. $\begin{array}{r} 8 \\ -\ 3 \\ \hline \end{array}$
8. $\begin{array}{r} 68 \\ -\ 3 \\ \hline \end{array}$

**Circle the tens. Write how many.**

9. 

______ ten

10. 

______ tens

# DAY 9

**Make the fact families.**

**1.** 7 + 1 = 8

____ + ____ = ____

____ − ____ = ____

____ − ____ = ____

**2.** 4 + 3 = 7

____ + ____ = ____

____ − ____ = ____

____ − ____ = ____

**Solve.**

**3.** There are 7 children in my family.
5 are boys.
How many are girls? ______ girls
Draw a picture to solve.

# DAY 10 CHECKPOINT

**Add or subtract.**

| **1.** | **2.** | **3.** | **4.** | **5.** | **6.** |
|---|---|---|---|---|---|
| 8 | 8 | 5 | 5 | 4 | 7 |
| − 5 | − 4 | + 2 | + 3 | + 4 | − 5 |

**Write the time.**

**7.**

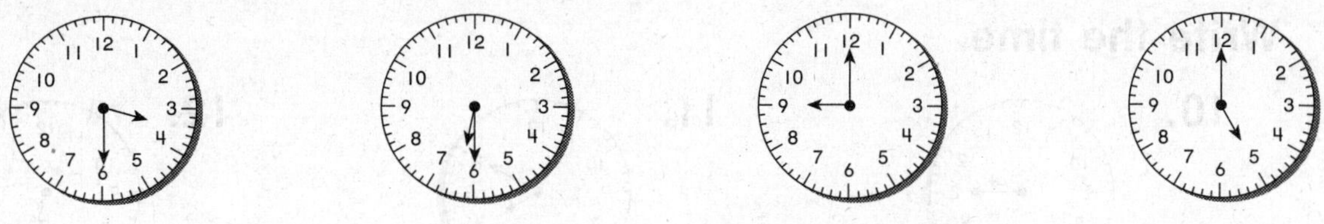

_ : _ _  _ : _ _  _ : _ _  _ : _ _

# DAY 11

**Add.**

1. $\begin{array}{r} 5 \\ +4 \\ \hline \end{array}$
2. $\begin{array}{r} 5 \\ +5 \\ \hline \end{array}$
3. $\begin{array}{r} 6 \\ +3 \\ \hline \end{array}$
4. $\begin{array}{r} 6 \\ +4 \\ \hline \end{array}$
5. $\begin{array}{r} 7 \\ +2 \\ \hline \end{array}$
6. $\begin{array}{r} 7 \\ +3 \\ \hline \end{array}$
7. $\begin{array}{r} 2 \\ +7 \\ \hline \end{array}$
8. $\begin{array}{r} 2 \\ +8 \\ \hline \end{array}$

**Continue the pattern.**

9. 8:00, 8:30, 9:00, ______, ______, ______, ______, ______

# DAY 12

**Subtract.**

1. $\begin{array}{r} 10 \\ -1 \\ \hline \end{array}$
2. $\begin{array}{r} 10 \\ -2 \\ \hline \end{array}$
3. $\begin{array}{r} 10 \\ -3 \\ \hline \end{array}$
4. $\begin{array}{r} 10 \\ -4 \\ \hline \end{array}$
5. $\begin{array}{r} 10 \\ -5 \\ \hline \end{array}$
6. $\begin{array}{r} 10 \\ -6 \\ \hline \end{array}$
7. $\begin{array}{r} 10 \\ -7 \\ \hline \end{array}$
8. $\begin{array}{r} 10 \\ -8 \\ \hline \end{array}$

**Count by 5's.**

9. 5, ____, ____, ____, ____, ____, ____, ____, ____, ____, ____

**Write the time.**

10. 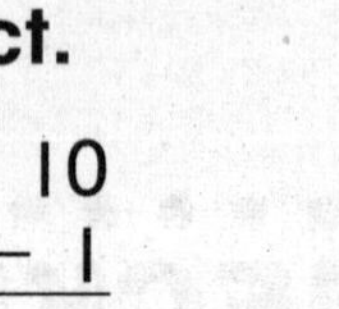

☐:☐☐

11. 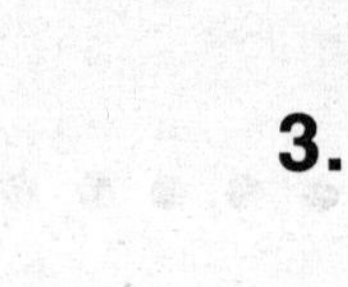

☐:☐☐

12. 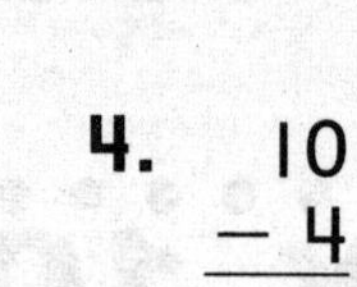

☐:☐☐

# DAY 13

**Add.**

**1.** 6 + 4 = ____ **2.** 3 + 2 = ____ **3.** 7 + 2 = ____ **4.** 6 + 2 = ____

**Subtract.**

**5.** 10 − 7 = ____ **6.** 8 − 4 = ____ **7.** 9 − 5 = ____ **8.** 10 − 5 = ____

**Make 2 triangles in a square.**
**Show how you did it.**

**9.**

# DAY 14

**Add.**

**1.**

| Number | 3 | 7 | 2 | 4 | 5 | 1 | 0 | 6 |
|---|---|---|---|---|---|---|---|---|
| + 3 | | | | | | | | |

**2.**

| Number | 10 | 7 | 5 | 8 | 4 | 6 | 9 | 3 | 2 |
|---|---|---|---|---|---|---|---|---|---|
| − 2 | | | | | | | | | |

**Look at the graph. Answer the questions.**

**3.** Are there more cats or dogs? ________

**4.** How many people have fish? _____

**5.** If 3 more children had dogs, how many dogs would there be? _____

**Our Pets**

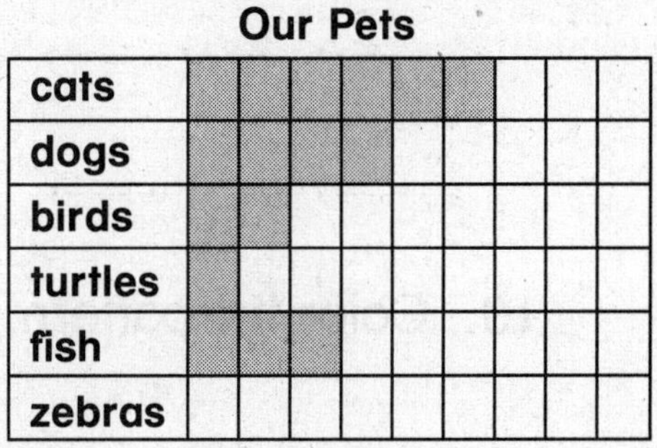

# DAY 15

**Subtract.**

**1.** 10 − 8 = ___ **2.** 30 − 8 = ___ **3.** 7 − 3 = ___ **4.** 27 − 3 = ___

**Add.**

**5.** 5 + 4 = ___ **6.** 55 + 4 = ___ **7.** 3 + 5 = ___ **8.** 43 + 5 = ___

**Choose 3 numbers.**
**Add 0.**

**9.** ___ + ___ = ___ **10.** ___ + ___ = ___ **11.** ___ + ___ = ___

**12.** When I add 0 to a number, ______________________.

# DAY 16

**Add.**

**1.** $\begin{array}{r} 7 \\ +\,3 \\ \hline \end{array}$ **2.** $\begin{array}{r} 9 \\ +\,1 \\ \hline \end{array}$ **3.** $\begin{array}{r} 8 \\ +\,2 \\ \hline \end{array}$ **4.** $\begin{array}{r} 3 \\ +\,4 \\ \hline \end{array}$ **5.** $\begin{array}{r} 6 \\ +\,3 \\ \hline \end{array}$ **6.** $\begin{array}{r} 4 \\ +\,5 \\ \hline \end{array}$ **7.** $\begin{array}{r} 6 \\ +\,4 \\ \hline \end{array}$ **8.** $\begin{array}{r} 2 \\ +\,7 \\ \hline \end{array}$

**Skip count by 3's.**

**9.** 3, 6, ___, ___, ___, ___,

___, ___, ___, ___, ___,

___, ___, ___, ___, ___

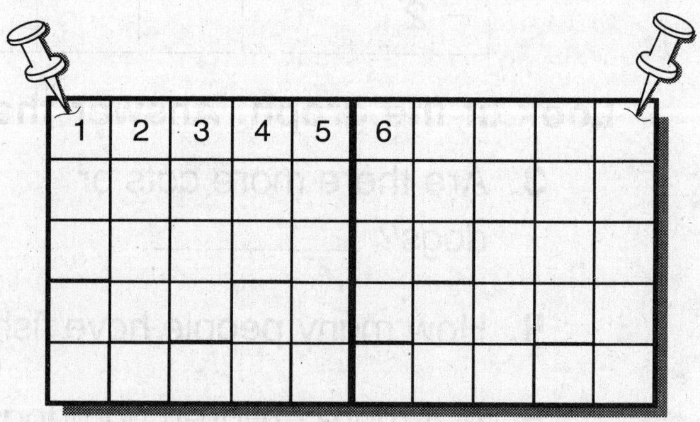


**10.** Color the pattern.

# Day 17

**Write 2 number sentences for each number.**

**1.** 10

___ + ___ = ___

___ − ___ = ___

**2.** 8

___ + ___ = ___

___ − ___ = ___

**3.** 9

___ + ___ = ___

___ − ___ = ___

**Match.**

**4.**

12:00 4:25 8:45 9:20

# Day 18

**Show 6 ways to make 8.**
**Add and subtract.**

**1.** ___ + ___ = ___ **2.** ___ + ___ = ___

**3.** ___ + ___ = ___ **4.** ___ + ___ = ___

**5.** ___ − ___ = ___ **6.** ___ − ___ = ___

**Write the numbers in order.**

**7.** 45, 43, 46, 44 ______, ______, ______, ______

**8.** 87, 89, 86, 88 ______, ______, ______, ______

# DAY 19

**Subtract.**

1. 9 − 5 = ___  2. 10 − 4 = ___  3. 8 − 6 = ___  4. 10 − 7 = ___

**Add.**

5. 6 + 4 = ___  6. 5 + 5 = ___  7. 4 + 4 = ___  8. 3 + 3 = ___

**Solve. Make the graph.**

9. Jon has a farm.
He has 5 chickens.
He has 2 cows.
He has 3 ducks.
Jon has _____ animals.

| | | |
|---|---|---|
| | | |
| | | |
| | | |
| | | |
| | | |
| **chickens** | **cows** | **ducks** |

# DAY 20

**Add.**

1. 2 + 7 = ___  2. 32 + 7 = ___  3. 52 + 7 = ___  4. 92 + 7 = ___

5. What pattern do you see? ______________________________
______________________________________________

**Write 3 numbers from the Calendar. Add 1 to each one.**

6. ___ + ___ = ___  7. ___ + ___ = ___  8. ___ + ___ = ___

9. **When I add 1 to an even number, the sum is ______.**

10. **When I add 1 to an odd number, the sum is ______.**

# MONTHLY ASSESSMENT

**Use the Calendar.**

1. Write the name of the month.

 ______________

2. How many days are in this month?

 ______

 How many were in September? ______

3. What date is the third Thursday of this month? ______________

4. What day is October 17? ____________

5. Name the shapes on the Calendar.

 ________________________________________

6. What do you notice about the rectangles? ____________

 ________________________________________

7. Describe the pattern of shapes. ____________

 Describe that pattern with letters? ____________

**Complete the pattern.**

8. ◯ ◯ ▯ ◯ ◯ ___ How do you know?

 ________________________________________

 ________________________________________

# MONTHLY ASSESSMENT

**Add.**

| 1. | 2. | 3. | 4. | 5. | 6. | 7. |
|---|---|---|---|---|---|---|
| 6 | 5 | 4 | 3 | 2 | 1 | 8 |
| + 4 | + 2 | + 5 | + 7 | + 6 | + 8 | + 2 |

| 8. | 9. | 10. | 11. | 12. | 13. | 14. |
|---|---|---|---|---|---|---|
| 3 | 6 | 9 | 5 | 7 | 10 | 4 |
| + 5 | + 3 | + 1 | + 1 | + 2 | + 0 | + 4 |

**Subtract.**

| 15. | 16. | 17. | 18. | 19. | 20. | 21. |
|---|---|---|---|---|---|---|
| 10 | 9 | 8 | 7 | 6 | 5 | 4 |
| − 2 | − 6 | − 5 | − 4 | − 2 | − 5 | − 0 |

| 22. | 23. | 24. | 25. | 26. | 27. | 28. |
|---|---|---|---|---|---|---|
| 10 | 8 | 7 | 9 | 10 | 8 | 6 |
| − 3 | − 2 | − 5 | − 4 | − 5 | − 4 | − 5 |

**Add.**

29.

| | 3 | 6 | 7 | 8 | 4 |
|---|---|---|---|---|---|
| +1 | 4 | | | | |

30.

| | 4 | 6 | 3 | 5 | 9 |
|---|---|---|---|---|---|
| +0 | 4 | | | | |

31. When I add 1 to a number, ______________________________

32. When I add 0 to a number, ______________________________

# MONTHLY ASSESSMENT

**Solve.**

1. Mario did 10 jumping jacks on Tuesday.
   He did 6 on Wednesday.
   How many more jumping jacks did he do on Tuesday than on Wednesday?

   _____ − _____ = _____

2. We go to school 5 days every week.
   We have been here 2 days this week.
   How many more days will we go to school this week?

   _____ days

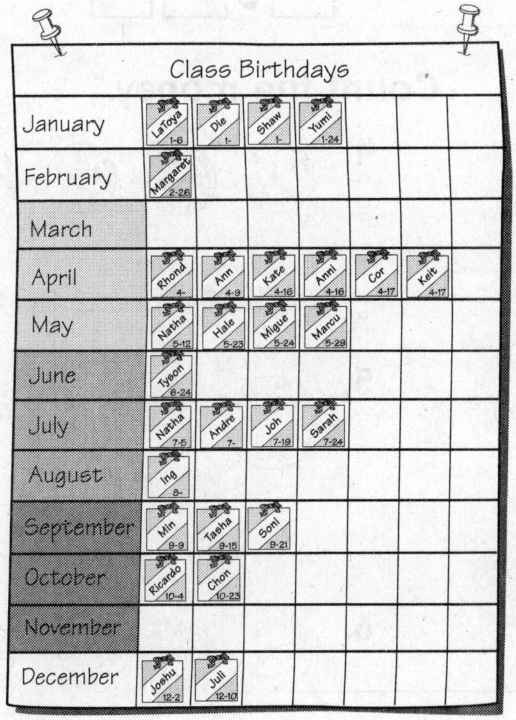


3. Are there birthdays every month? __________

4. Which months have no birthdays?

   ____________________

5. Which month has the most birthdays?

   __________

6. In which months are there 4 birthdays? ____________________

7. Are there birthdays on the graph in your birthday month?

   ______________________________

   What month is your birthday? ____________________

8. How many birthdays are in the summer? __________

# MONTHLY ASSESSMENT

**Match.**

**1.** 

**2.** 

**3.** 

6:10    4:00    3:20

**Count the money.**

**4.** 

_____¢, _____¢, _____¢, _____¢, _____¢, _____¢

**5.** 

_____¢, _____¢, _____¢, _____¢, _____¢, _____¢, _____¢

**6.** 

_____¢, _____¢, _____¢, _____¢, _____¢

**Match the same shapes.**

**7.** 

**8.** 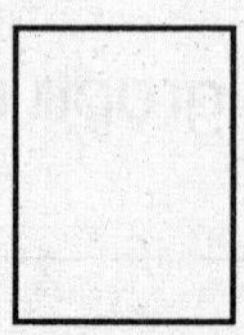

**9.** 

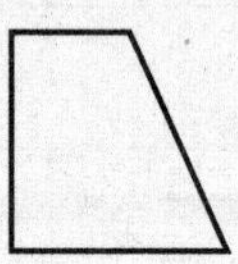

# DAY 1 NOVEMBER

**Count on.**
**Add.**

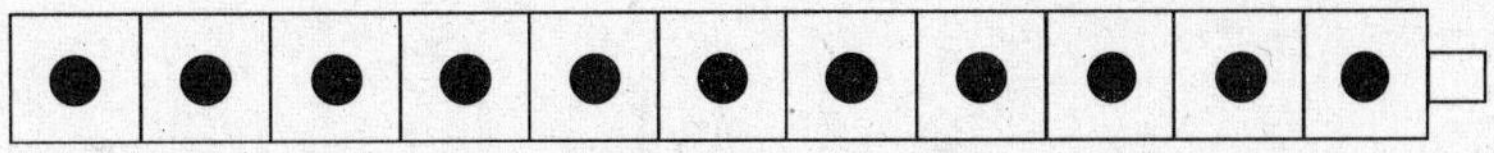

1 2 3 4 5 6 7 8 9 10 11 .

1. 2 more than 9 is ______. $9 + 2 =$ ______
2. 3 more than 8 is ______. $8 + 3 =$ ______
3. 4 more than 7 is ______. $7 + 4 =$ ______

**Continue the pattern.**

4. $7 + 4 = 11$

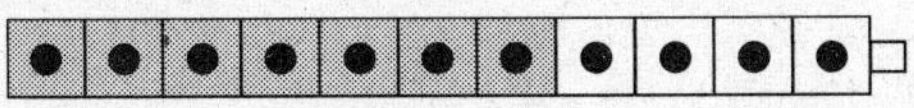

$8 + 3 =$ ____

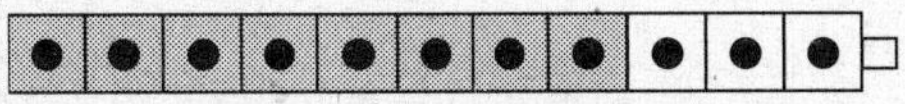

____ + ____ = ____

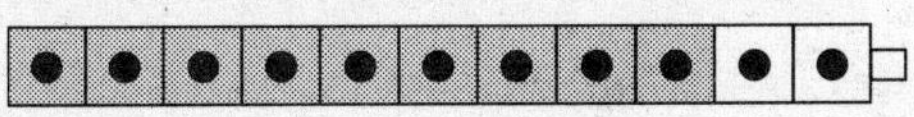

____ + ____ = ____

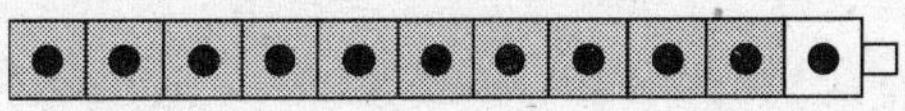

5. What do you see? ______________________________________________

______________________________________________________________

# DAY 2

**Add.**

1. $\begin{array}{r} 7 \\ +\,4 \\ \hline \end{array}$ 2. $\begin{array}{r} 4 \\ +\,7 \\ \hline \end{array}$ 3. $\begin{array}{r} 8 \\ +\,3 \\ \hline \end{array}$ 4. $\begin{array}{r} 3 \\ +\,8 \\ \hline \end{array}$ 5. $\begin{array}{r} 9 \\ +\,2 \\ \hline \end{array}$ 6. $\begin{array}{r} 2 \\ +\,9 \\ \hline \end{array}$

**Write the time.**

7. 

______

I go to school.

8. 

______

It is lunch time.

9. 

______

It is recess.

10. 

______

I go home.

# Day 3

**Make 11.**

1. ___ + ___ = 11  2. ___ + ___ = 11  3. ___ + ___ = 11

4. ___ + ___ = 11  5. ___ + ___ = 11  6. ___ + ___ = 11

**I am a shape.**
**Write my name. Draw me.**

7. I am round. ___________
8. I have 3 sides. ___________
9. I have 4 equal sides. ___________

# Day 4

**Add.**

1. 4 + 5 = ___  2. 5 + 5 = ___  3. 6 + 5 = ___  4. 3 + 5 = ___

5. 7 + 3 = ___  6. 2 + 9 = ___  7. 3 + 8 = ___  8. 1 + 7 = ___

**Solve. Use the 10 grid.**

9. The zoo had 7 seals.
They bought 4 more.
How many seals
do they have now?
______ seals

# DAY 5

**Add.**

1. $\begin{array}{r} 7 \\ +\ 3 \\ \hline \end{array}$ 2. $\begin{array}{r} 6 \\ +\ 5 \\ \hline \end{array}$ 3. $\begin{array}{r} 8 \\ +\ 3 \\ \hline \end{array}$ 4. $\begin{array}{r} 10 \\ +\ 1 \\ \hline \end{array}$ 5. $\begin{array}{r} 11 \\ +\ 0 \\ \hline \end{array}$ 6. $\begin{array}{r} 2 \\ +\ 9 \\ \hline \end{array}$ 7. $\begin{array}{r} 1 \\ +\ 7 \\ \hline \end{array}$

**Make 10.**
**Write the new number sentence.**

8. 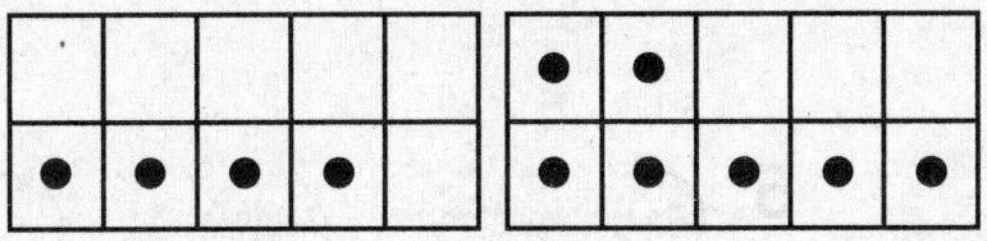

$4 + 7 =$ ______

$10 +$ ______ $=$ ______

9. 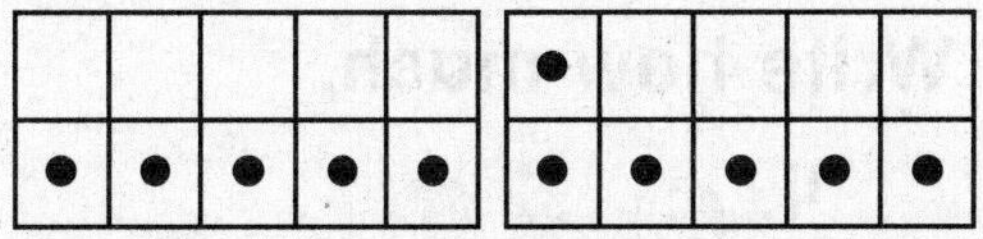

______ $+$ ______ $=$ ______

______ $+$ ______ $=$ ______

# DAY 6

**Count back. Use the cubes.**
**Write the number sentence.**

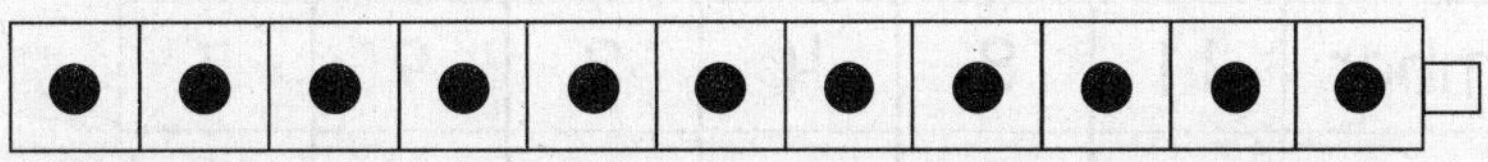

**1 2 3 4 5 6 7 8 9 10 11**

1. 3 less than 11 is ______. $11 - 3 =$ ______

2. 6 less than 11 is ______. $11 -$ ______ $=$ ______

3. 1 less than 11 is ______. ______ $-$ ______ $=$ ______

4. 5 less than 11 is ______. ______ $-$ ______ $=$ ______

**Continue the pattern.**

5. 22, 24, 26, ______, ______, ______, ______

# DAY 7

**Make fact families for 11.**

1. ___ + ___ = ___
   ___ + ___ = ___
   ___ − ___ = ___
   ___ − ___ = ___

2. ___ + ___ = ___
   ___ + ___ = ___
   ___ − ___ = ___
   ___ − ___ = ___

3. ___ + ___ = ___
   ___ + ___ = ___
   ___ − ___ = ___
   ___ − ___ = ___

**Write how much.**

4. 

___ ¢

5. 

___ ¢

# DAY 8

**Complete the tables.**

1.

| Number | 11 | 8 | 4 | 3 | 9 | 7 |
|---|---|---|---|---|---|---|
| − 3 | | | | | | |

2.

| Number | 11 | 7 | 5 | 9 | 10 | 6 |
|---|---|---|---|---|---|---|
| − 5 | | | | | | |

**Write the number.**

3. 8 tens and 4 ones ___
4. 4 tens and 0 ones ___
5. 6 tens and 3 ones ___
6. 5 tens and 5 ones ___
7. Write the numbers in order.

___, ___, ___, ___

# Day 9

**Add.**

1. $8 + 3$
2. $3 + 8$
3. $5 + 6$
4. $6 + 5$
5. $7 + 2$
6. $2 + 7$
7. $3 + 7$
8. $7 + 3$

**Solve.**

9. Cows have 4 feet. Chickens have 2 feet. How many feet do 5 cows and 4 chickens have? _______ feet
Show how you got your answer.

# Day 10 CHECKPOINT

**Add or subtract.**

1. $6 + 5$
2. $11 - 5$
3. $11 - 6$
4. $5 + 6$
5. $4 + 7$
6. $7 + 4$
7. $11 - 4$
8. $11 - 7$

**Show the time.**

9. 6:00 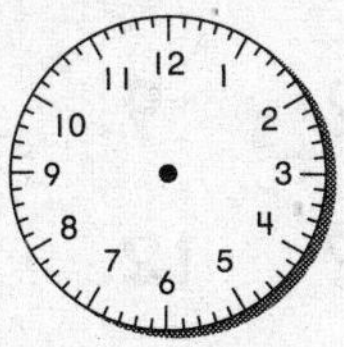

10. 6:15 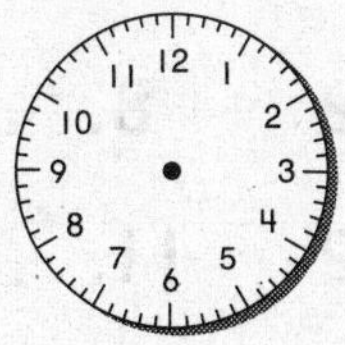

11. 6:30 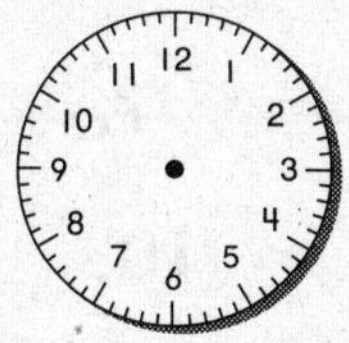

**Write how much.**

12. 

_______¢

13. 

_______¢

# DAY 11

**Add.**

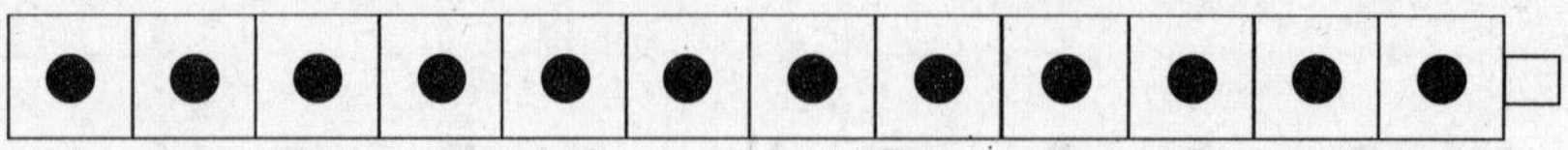

1 2 3 4 5 6 7 8 9 10 11 12

| 1. | 2. | 3. | 4. | 5. | 6. | 7. | 8. |
|---|---|---|---|---|---|---|---|
| 2 | 10 | 3 | 9 | 4 | 8 | 5 | 7 |
| + 10 | + 2 | + 9 | + 3 | + 8 | + 4 | + 7 | + 5 |

**Continue the pattern.**

9. 7 + 5 = 12     8 + 4 = 12

___ + ___ = ___    ___ + ___ = ___    ___ + ___ = ___

10. What happens when the first addend gets bigger? ____________________

______________________________________________

# DAY 12

**Show ways to make 12.**

1. ___ + ___ = 12    2. ___ + ___ = 12    3. ___ + ___ = 12

4. ___ + ___ = 12    5. ___ + ___ = 12    6. ___ + ___ = 12

7. ___ + ___ = 12    8. ___ + ___ = 12    9. ___ + ___ = 12

10. ___ + ___ = 12    11. ___ + ___ = 12    12. ___ + ___ = 12

**Can you buy it? Circle yes or no.**

13.

yes    no

14.

yes    no

# DAY 13

**Count up to 12.**

1. 4 + ___ = 12  2. 5 + ___ = 12  3. 6 + ___ = 12  4. 7 + ___ = 12

5. 8 + ___ = 12  6. 9 + ___ = 12  7. 10 + ___ = 12  8. 11 + ___ = 12

**Draw 3 different shapes with 4 edges and 4 corners.**

9.

# DAY 14

**Add.**
**Circle fact pairs.**

1. $\begin{array}{r} 9 \\ +\ 3 \\ \hline \end{array}$  2. $\begin{array}{r} 5 \\ +\ 7 \\ \hline \end{array}$  3. $\begin{array}{r} 4 \\ +\ 8 \\ \hline \end{array}$  4. $\begin{array}{r} 6 \\ +\ 6 \\ \hline \end{array}$  5. $\begin{array}{r} 8 \\ +\ 4 \\ \hline \end{array}$  6. $\begin{array}{r} 2 \\ +10 \\ \hline \end{array}$  7. $\begin{array}{r} 1 \\ +11 \\ \hline \end{array}$

8. $\begin{array}{r} 7 \\ +\ 5 \\ \hline \end{array}$  9. $\begin{array}{r} 3 \\ +\ 9 \\ \hline \end{array}$  10. $\begin{array}{r} 12 \\ +\ 0 \\ \hline \end{array}$  11. $\begin{array}{r} 0 \\ +12 \\ \hline \end{array}$  12. $\begin{array}{r} 11 \\ +\ 1 \\ \hline \end{array}$  13. $\begin{array}{r} 10 \\ +\ 2 \\ \hline \end{array}$

14. Why doesn't 6 + 6 have a fact pair partner? ______________

**Solve.**

15. There are 12 children on the team.
9 children can play at any one time.
How many children must wait? ______ children
Show your work. ______________

# DAY 15

**Add.**
**Write the matching fact.**

**1.** 7 + 5 = __ **2.** 8 + 3 = __ **3.** 6 + 4 = __ **4.** 2 + 8 = __

__ + __ = __ __ + __ = __ __ + __ = __ __ + __ = __

**5.** How do fact pairs help you learn your facts? ____________________

____________________

**Solve.**

**6.** I have 7 coins in my pocket. They are dimes, nickels, and pennies.
When I counted them, I had 38¢.
What coins might I have in my pocket? ____________________

____________________

**7.** How did you find out? ____________________

# DAY 16

**Subtract.**

**1.** 12 − 1 = ____ **2.** 12 − 2 = ____ **3.** 12 − 3 = ____

**4.** 12 − 4 = ____ **5.** 12 − 5 = ____ **6.** 12 − 6 = ____

**7.** 12 − 7 = ____ **8.** 12 − 8 = ____ **9.** 12 − 9 = ____

**Color the numbers that have 0 or 5 in the ones place.**

**10.**

| 1 | 2 | 3 | 4 | 5 | 6 | 7 | 8 | 9 | 10 |
|---|---|---|---|---|---|---|---|---|---|
| 11 | 12 | 13 | 14 | 15 | 16 | 17 | 18 | 19 | 20 |
| 21 | 22 | 23 | 24 | 25 | 26 | 27 | 28 | 29 | 30 |
| | | | | | | | | | |

**11.** What do you see?

____________________

____________________

# DAY 17

**Make fact families for 12.**

1. ____ + ____ = ____
   ____ + ____ = ____
   ____ − ____ = ____
   ____ − ____ = ____

2. ____ + ____ = ____
   ____ + ____ = ____
   ____ − ____ = ____
   ____ − ____ = ____

**Draw the hands. Write the time.**

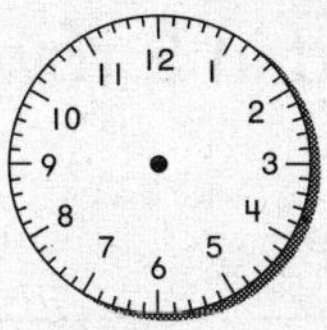


**3.** I get up.
It is ____.

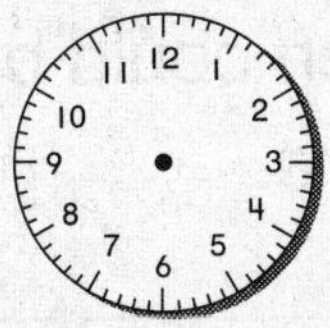


**4.** I go to school.
It is ____.

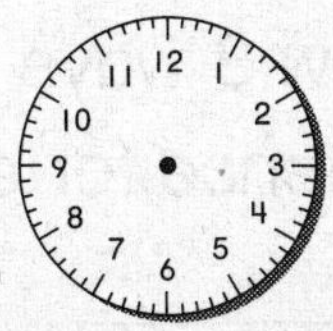


**5.** I go to recess.
It is ____.

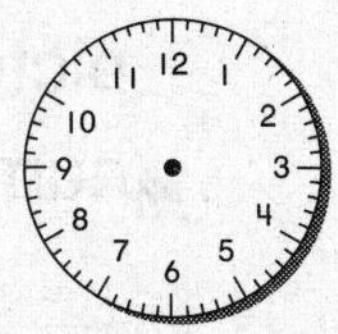


**6.** I go to bed.
It is ____.

# DAY 18

**Subtract.**

**1.** 12 − ____ = 3 **2.** 12 − ____ = 9 **3.** 12 − ____ = 8 **4.** 12 − ____ = 4

**5.** 12 − ____ = 6 **6.** 12 − ____ = 5 **7.** 12 − ____ = 7 **8.** 12 − ____ = 2

**9.** How did you find the differences? ________________________________

________________________________________________

________________________________________________

**Put the numbers in order.**

**10.** 78 52 99 13 46 24 89 31

____ ____ ____ ____ ____ ____ ____ ____

# DAY 19

**Make 1 addition and 1 subtraction fact for each pair of numbers.**

**1.** 3, 9

___ + ___ = ___

___ − ___ = ___

**2.** 8, 4

___ + ___ = ___

___ − ___ = ___

**3.** 6, 5

___ + ___ = ___

___ − ___ = ___

**Solve.**

**4.** There are 12 children on the team. All children must be in the team picture. Show 3 ways the children could be placed in 2 rows. Write a number sentence for each picture.

______________________________

______________________________

______________________________

# DAY 20

**Add or subtract.**

**1.** $12 - 5$ **2.** $3 + 9$ **3.** $7 + 5$ **4.** $12 - 8$ **5.** $6 + 6$ **6.** $12 - 4$ **7.** $12 - 9$ **8.** $10 + 2$

**9.** $12 - 5$ **10.** $4 + 8$ **11.** $5 + 7$ **12.** $12 - 2$ **13.** $9 + 3$ **14.** $12 - 3$ **15.** $12 - 8$ **16.** $2 + 10$

**Use your classroom Calendar.**

**17.** How many weeks are there this month? ______________

**18.** What day of the week was November 1? ______________

**19.** How many days are in November? ______________

# MONTHLY ASSESSMENT

**Use the Calendar.**

1. What is the name month? ____________

2. How many days are in this month? ______

3. Name another month with 30 days

   ____________________________

4. What day of the week was November 1?

   ______________

5. Describe the shapes on the calendar.

   ____________________________________________

6. Describe the pattern with letters. ____________

7. Which shape is on 3, 6, 9, and 12? ______________

8. Which of these shapes roll? ______________

   Which of these shapes stack? ______________________

   Which of these shapes slide? ______________________

9. Julie has soccer practice every Tuesday. What are the dates?

   ______________________________

10. Karen has soccer practice every Sunday. Does she have more practices in November than Julie?

    ____________________________________________

# MONTHLY ASSESSMENT

**Add.**

| | | | | | | | |
|---|---|---|---|---|---|---|---|
| **1.** $5 + 6$ | **2.** $7 + 4$ | **3.** $8 + 3$ | **4.** $9 + 3$ | **5.** $10 + 2$ | **6.** $11 + 1$ | **7.** $12 + 0$ | **8.** $7 + 5$ |
| **9.** $4 + 8$ | **10.** $5 + 4$ | **11.** $6 + 6$ | **12.** $7 + 3$ | **13.** $8 + 2$ | **14.** $9 + 1$ | **15.** $10 + 1$ | **16.** $2 + 8$ |

**Subtract.**

| | | | | | | | |
|---|---|---|---|---|---|---|---|
| **17.** $10 - 8$ | **18.** $11 - 3$ | **19.** $12 - 4$ | **20.** $10 - 5$ | **21.** $11 - 7$ | **22.** $12 - 6$ | **23.** $10 - 9$ | **24.** $12 - 3$ |
| **25.** $8 - 6$ | **26.** $9 - 2$ | **27.** $10 - 7$ | **28.** $11 - 6$ | **29.** $12 - 7$ | **30.** $10 - 8$ | **31.** $7 - 6$ | **32.** $8 - 7$ |

**Add or subtract.**

| | | | | | | | |
|---|---|---|---|---|---|---|---|
| **33.** $3 + 3$ | **34.** $4 + 4$ | **35.** $5 + 5$ | **36.** $6 + 6$ | **37.** $12 - 6$ | **38.** $10 - 5$ | **39.** $8 - 4$ | **40.** $6 - 3$ |

**Make the fact families.**

| **41.** $5 + 7 = 12$ | **42.** $3 + 8 = 11$ |
|---|---|
| ____ + ____ = ____ | ____ + ____ = ____ |
| ____ − ____ = ____ | ____ − ____ = ____ |
| ____ − ____ = ____ | ____ − ____ = ____ |

# MONTHLY ASSESSMENT

**Use the graph to answer.**

| Favorite Color | | | | | | | | | | |
|---|---|---|---|---|---|---|---|---|---|---|
| **Blue** | X | X | X | X | X | X | X | X | | |
| **Yellow** | X | X | X | X | | | | | | |
| **Green** | X | X | | | | | | | | |
| **Purple** | X | X | X | X | X | X | X | X | X | |

1. Which color did more people like? ________

2. Which was the least favorite color? ________

3. How many more people liked purple than liked green? ________

4. How many people liked green and yellow? ________

5. What is your favorite color? ________________
   Put it on the graph.

**Solve.**

6. Jon read 11 books this month.
   He read 3 more books than last month.
   How many books did he read last month? ________________

7. Pete collects shells.
   In one box, he has 7 large shells.
   In another box, he has 3 medium shells.
   How many shells does he have? ________
   Show how you found out.

# Monthly Assessment

**Can you buy it?**
**Circle yes or no.**

**1.** 

yes no

**2.** 

yes no

**3.** 

yes no

**Write the time and put the clocks in order.**

**4.** ____ 

**5.** ____ 

**6.** ____ 

☐:☐☐ ☐:☐☐ ☐:☐☐

**Draw the shapes.**

**7.** 3 sides and 3 corners
4 sides and 4 corners
4 equal sides and 4 corners

# DAY 1 DECEMBER

**Add.**

| 1. | 2. | 3. | 4. | 5. | 6. |
|---|---|---|---|---|---|
| $\begin{array}{r}1\\+1\\\hline\end{array}$ | $\begin{array}{r}2\\+2\\\hline\end{array}$ | $\begin{array}{r}3\\+3\\\hline\end{array}$ | $\begin{array}{r}4\\+4\\\hline\end{array}$ | $\begin{array}{r}5\\+5\\\hline\end{array}$ | $\begin{array}{r}6\\+6\\\hline\end{array}$ |

| 7. | 8. | 9. | 10. | 11. | 12. |
|---|---|---|---|---|---|
| $\begin{array}{r}1\\+2\\\hline\end{array}$ | $\begin{array}{r}2\\+3\\\hline\end{array}$ | $\begin{array}{r}3\\+4\\\hline\end{array}$ | $\begin{array}{r}4\\+5\\\hline\end{array}$ | $\begin{array}{r}5\\+6\\\hline\end{array}$ | $\begin{array}{r}6\\+7\\\hline\end{array}$ |

**Notice the pattern.**

13. The sums of doubles are ____________ numbers.

14. The sums of doubles + 1 are ____________ numbers.

# DAY 2

**Write the number sentences.**

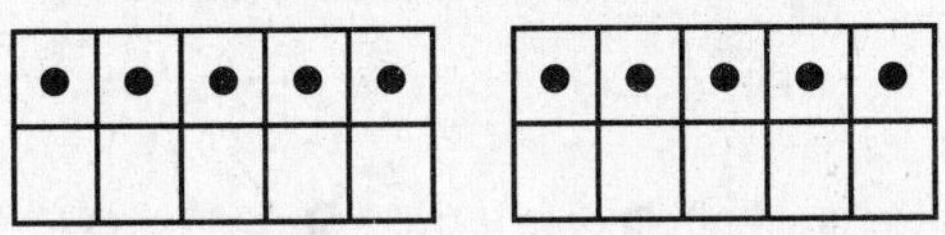

1. _____ + _____ = _____

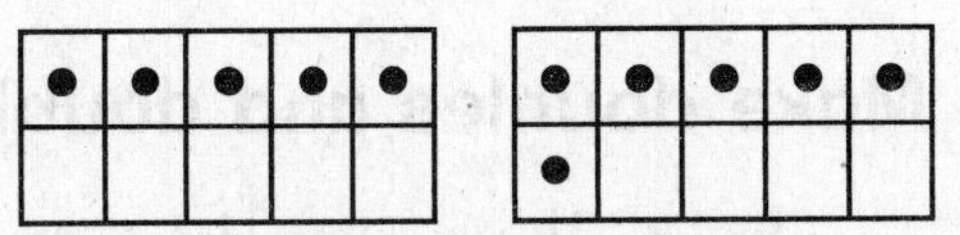

2. _____ + _____ = _____

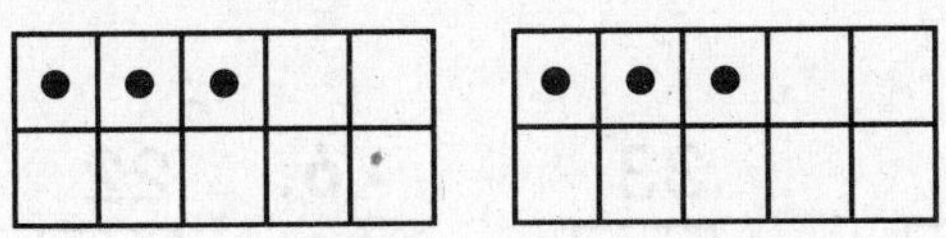

3. _____ + _____ = _____

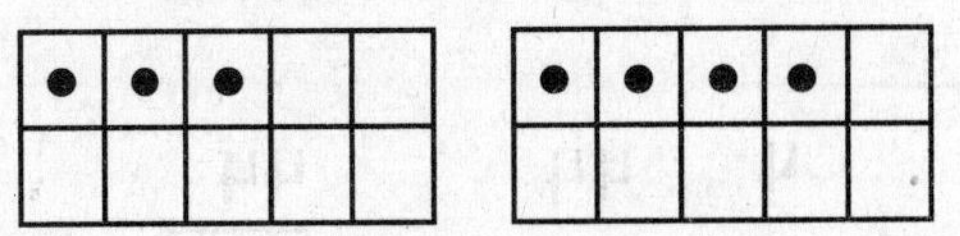

4. _____ + _____ = _____

**Draw an X on the coins.**

5. 42¢

6. 38¢

7. 61¢

# DAY 3

**Circle the doubles and the doubles + 1 pairs.**

1. $6 + 6$
2. $3 + 4$
3. $2 + 3$
4. $5 + 5$
5. $4 + 5$
6. $1 + 1$
7. $3 + 3$
8. $6 + 7$
9. $2 + 2$
10. $5 + 6$
11. $1 + 2$
12. $4 + 4$

**Circle similar shapes.**

13. 

# DAY 4

**Make doubles and doubles + 1.**

1. $4 + \square$ $4 + \square$
2. $3 + \square$ $3 + \square$
3. $2 + \square$ $2 + \square$
4. $44 + 44$ $44 + \square$
5. $33 + \square$ $33 + \square$
6. $22 + \square$ $22 + \square$

**Solve.**

7. Bill has 3 green cars and 4 red cars. How many cars does he have?
   ______ cars

   If he gives 1 car to Sam, how many cars will he have? ______ cars

# DAY 5

**Add the doubles + 1. Write the doubles and add.**

**1.** $\begin{array}{r} 5 \\ +\ 6 \\ \hline \end{array}$ $\begin{array}{r} \square \\ +\ \square \\ \hline \end{array}$ **2.** $\begin{array}{r} 4 \\ +\ 5 \\ \hline \end{array}$ $\begin{array}{r} \square \\ +\ \square \\ \hline \end{array}$ **3.** $\begin{array}{r} 6 \\ +\ 7 \\ \hline \end{array}$ $\begin{array}{r} \square \\ +\ \square \\ \hline \end{array}$ **4.** $\begin{array}{r} 3 \\ +\ 4 \\ \hline \end{array}$ $\begin{array}{r} \square \\ +\ \square \\ \hline \end{array}$

**Look at the December Calendar.**

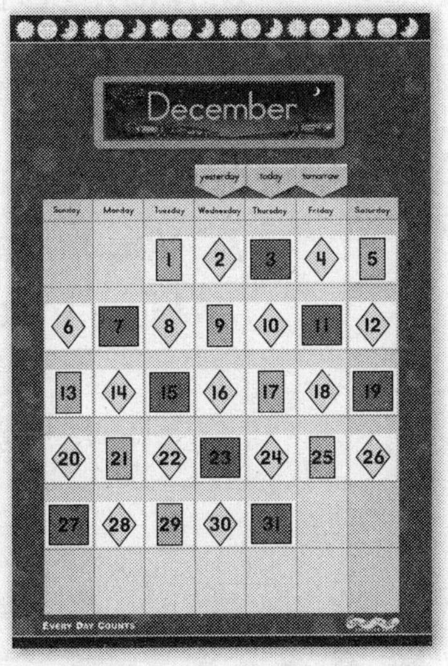


**5.** Find 8 doubles. ______________________

______________________________________

**6.** Find 8 doubles + 1. ________________

______________________________________

# DAY 6

**Add.**

**1.** 20 + 20 = _____ **2.** 20 + 21 = _____ **3.** 43 + 43 = _____

**4.** 43 + 44 = _____ **5.** 25 + 25 = _____ **6.** 25 + 26 = _____

**Write < or >.**

**7.** 63 ◯ 42 **8.** 57 ◯ 75 **9.** 22 ◯ 32

**Complete the pattern.**

**10.** ↑ ↓ → ↑ ↑ ↓ → ↑ _____ _____ _____ _____

# DAY 7

**Add.**

| 1. | 2. | 3. | 4. | 5. |
|---|---|---|---|---|
| $\begin{array}{r} 23 \\ + 44 \\ \hline \end{array}$ | $\begin{array}{r} 44 \\ + 35 \\ \hline \end{array}$ | $\begin{array}{r} 72 \\ + 13 \\ \hline \end{array}$ | $\begin{array}{r} 61 \\ + 32 \\ \hline \end{array}$ | $\begin{array}{r} 54 \\ + 15 \\ \hline \end{array}$ |

6. How can double + 1 help you add? ______________________

______________________________________________

**Solve.**

7. You have 75¢. You buy a bag of chips for 35¢.
How much money do you have now? ______¢

Show how you found your answer. ______________________

______________________________________________

# DAY 8

**Add.**

| 1. | 2. | 3. | 4. | 5. | 6. | 7. |
|---|---|---|---|---|---|---|
| $\begin{array}{r} 7 \\ + 7 \\ \hline \end{array}$ | $\begin{array}{r} 5 \\ + 6 \\ \hline \end{array}$ | $\begin{array}{r} 3 \\ + 4 \\ \hline \end{array}$ | $\begin{array}{r} 3 \\ + 3 \\ \hline \end{array}$ | $\begin{array}{r} 1 \\ + 2 \\ \hline \end{array}$ | $\begin{array}{r} 2 \\ + 2 \\ \hline \end{array}$ | $\begin{array}{r} 8 \\ + 8 \\ \hline \end{array}$ |

| 8. | 9. | 10. | 11. | 12. | 13. | 14. |
|---|---|---|---|---|---|---|
| $\begin{array}{r} 8 \\ + 9 \\ \hline \end{array}$ | $\begin{array}{r} 6 \\ + 6 \\ \hline \end{array}$ | $\begin{array}{r} 6 \\ + 7 \\ \hline \end{array}$ | $\begin{array}{r} 4 \\ + 4 \\ \hline \end{array}$ | $\begin{array}{r} 4 \\ + 5 \\ \hline \end{array}$ | $\begin{array}{r} 5 \\ + 5 \\ \hline \end{array}$ | $\begin{array}{r} 7 \\ + 8 \\ \hline \end{array}$ |

**Write the numbers.**

15. I have 7 in the 10's place. The sum of my 2 digits is 9. I am _____.

16. I have 4 in the 1's place. The digit in the 10's place is 5 less than 12.
I am _____.

# DAY 9

**Add. Circle the doubles + 1.**

| 1. | 2. | 3. | 4. | 5. |
|---|---|---|---|---|
| $5 + 4$ | $7 + 5$ | $9 + 3$ | $6 + 6$ | $5 + 7$ |

| 6. | 7. | 8. | 9. |
|---|---|---|---|
| $6 + 4$ | $3 + 4$ | $8 + 4$ | $2 + 3$ |

**Solve.**

10. Kisha bought a doll for 25¢ and a pin for 10¢. She paid 2 quarters. How much change will she get? ______¢

# DAY 10 CHECKPOINT

**Write the doubles.**

1. ___ + ___ = 12
2. ___ + ___ = 8
3. ___ + ___ = 6
4. ___ + ___ = 4
5. ___ + ___ = 10
6. ___ + ___ = 2

**Write the doubles + 1.**

7. ___ + ___ = 9
8. ___ + ___ = 13
9. ___ + ___ = 7
10. ___ + ___ = 3
11. ___ + ___ = 5
12. ___ + ___ = 11

**Write < or >.**

13. 49 ◯ 76
14. 89 ◯ 73
15. 96 ◯ 98
16. Write your own. ______ ◯ ______

# DAY 11

**Add.**

1. 73 + 13 = ____ 2. 44 + 15 = ____ 3. 22 + 73 = ____

4. 51 + 22 = ____ 5. 82 + 12 = ____ 6. 54 + 44 = ____

**Describe the pattern.**

7. Color all the doubles. What patterns do you see? ______________________

______________________

| 1 | 2 | 3 | 4 | 5 | 6 | 7 | 8 | 9 | 10 |
|---|---|---|---|---|---|---|---|---|---|
| 11 | 12 | 13 | 14 | 15 | 16 | 17 | 18 | 19 | 20 |
| 21 | 22 | 23 | 24 | 25 | 26 | 27 | 28 | 29 | 30 |
| 31 | 32 | 33 | 34 | 35 | 36 | 37 | 38 | 39 | 40 |
| 41 | 42 | 43 | 44 | 45 | 46 | 47 | 48 | 49 | 50 |

# DAY 12

**Add.**
**Circle the sums that are even.**

1. 1 + 4
2. 5 + 6
3. 3 + 2
4. 8 + 4
5. 9 + 3
6. 6 + 5
7. 31 + 34
8. 55 + 24
9. 33 + 22
10. 28 + 11
11. 49 + 30
12. 76 + 23

**Complete.**

| | I spend | I pay | My change is |
|---|---|---|---|
| 13. | 23 cents | 3 dimes | ______¢ |
| 14. | 50 cents | 2 quarters | ______¢ |
| 15. | 89 cents | 2 quarters, 4 dimes | ______¢ |

# DAY 13

**Add.**
**Circle the doubles.**

1. $4 + 4$
2. $4 + 5$
3. $5 + 5$
4. $5 + 6$
5. $6 + 6$
6. $6 + 7$
7. $7 + 7$
8. $7 + 8$
9. $8 + 8$

10. Ana says that if you add 2 to a double, you get another double. Do you think she is right? Use the problems above to help explain your answer. ____________________

**Draw 2 different shapes that have 4 equal sides.**

11.

# DAY 14

**Make the double and add both facts.**

1. $4 + 5 = 9$ $\square + \square = 8$
2. $3 + 4 = 7$ $\square + \square = 6$
3. $7 + 8 = 15$ $\square + \square = 14$
4. $5 + \square = 11$ $\square + \square = 10$

**Solve.**

5. Li went to the class store and bought a pencil for 7¢ and an eraser for 8¢. He paid with a quarter.
How much change will he get back? ______¢
How did you find out? ____________________

# DAY 15

**Make doubles and doubles + I pairs.**

I. ___ + ___ = ___   2. ___ + ___ = ___   3. ___ + ___ = ___

___ + ___ = ___   ___ + ___ = ___   ___ + ___ = ___

4. ___ + ___ = ___   5. ___ + ___ = ___   6. ___ + ___ = ___

___ + ___ = ___   ___ + ___ = ___   ___ + ___ = ___

**Circle the digit in the tens place.**

**7.** 79 **8.** 64 **9.** 89 **10.** 53 **II.** 15 **12.** 49 **13.** 66

**Use the chart.**

**I4.** What number has 6 in the ones place and is 3 more than 43? ______

**I5.** What number is 2 tens bigger than 30? ______

| 1 | 2 | 3 | 4 | 5 | 6 | 7 | 8 | 9 | 10 |
|---|---|---|---|---|---|---|---|---|---|
| 11 | 12 | 13 | 14 | 15 | 16 | 17 | 18 | 19 | 20 |
| 21 | 22 | 23 | 24 | 25 | 26 | 27 | 28 | 29 | 30 |
| 31 | 32 | 33 | 34 | 35 | 36 | 37 | 38 | 39 | 40 |
| 41 | 42 | 43 | 44 | 45 | 46 | 47 | 48 | 49 | 50 |

**I6.** This number has the same digit in the tens place and in the ones place. The sum of the digits is 4. What's the number? ______

**I7.** This number has a 4 in the ones place. It is larger than 24, but smaller than 44. If you add the digits, you get a sum of 7. What number is it? ______

**Complete.**

**I8.** I have 4 coins in my pocket. What is the largest amount of money I can have in my pocket? ______________________

______________________________________

What is the smallest amount of money? ______________

# MONTHLY ASSESSMENT

**Use the Calendar.**

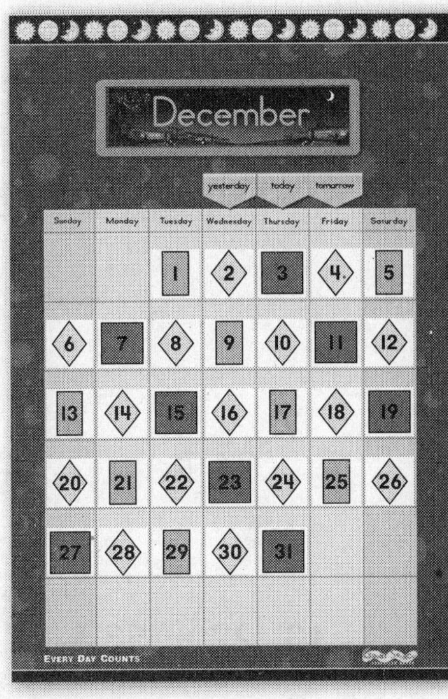


**1.** Write the name of the month.

______________________

**2.** How many days are in this month? ______

**3.** Name another month with 31 days.

__________________________________________

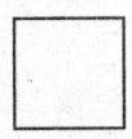

**4.** Name these shapes. __________________

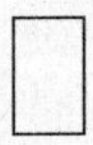

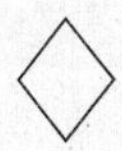

__________________ __________________

**5.** How are these shapes alike? ______________________________________

______________________________________________________________

**6.** What do we call a four sided closed figure? _________________________

**7.** How are squares and rhombuses alike? _____________________________

______________________________________________________________

**8.** List the numbers on the rhombuses. ____, ____, ____, ____,

____, ____, ____, ____, ____, ____, ____, ____, ____, ____

How are they alike? ________________________________________________

**9.** On what day will January 1 be? ______________________

# MONTHLY ASSESSMENT

**Add.**

**Draw lines to match the doubles and the doubles + 1.**

**1.** $1 + 1$ = ____ **2.** $3 + 3$ = ____ **3.** $5 + 5$ = ____ **4.** $6 + 6$ = ____ **5.** $4 + 4$ = ____ **6.** $2 + 2$ = ____

**7.** $4 + 5$ = ____ **8.** $2 + 3$ = ____ **9.** $6 + 7$ = ____ **10.** $5 + 6$ = ____ **11.** $3 + 4$ = ____ **12.** $1 + 2$ = ____

**13.** 22 + 53 = ______ **14.** 44 + 25 = ______ **15.** 31 + 62 = ______

**Write the doubles + 1.**

**16.** $2 + 2$ = ____ ; $2 + \square$ = ____

**17.** $4 + 4$ = ____ ; $4 + \square$ = ____

**18.** $6 + 6$ = ____ ; $6 + \square$ = ____

**19.** $3 + 3$ = ____ ; $3 + \square$ = ____

**20.** Are the sums of doubles always even numbers? Explain your thinking. ________________________________

________________________________

**21.** Are the sums of doubles + 1 even or odd? Why? ________________

________________________________

**Write < or >.**

**22.** 69 ◯ 59 **23.** 71 ◯ 86 **24.** 59 ◯ 61 **25.** 18 ◯ 8

# MONTHLY ASSESSMENT

**Make a graph.**

The zoo has 7 seals, 5 monkeys, 1 hippo, 3 elephants, and 4 giraffes.

| Seal | | | | | | | | |
|---|---|---|---|---|---|---|---|---|
| Monkey | | | | | | | | |
| Hippo | | | | | | | | |
| Elephant | | | | | | | | |
| Giraffe | | | | | | | | |

1. The zoo has more __________ than any other animal.
2. How many more monkeys are there than elephants? _____
3. How many monkeys and seals are there? _____
4. How many elephants and giraffes are there? _____
5. How many more seals are there than monkeys? _____
6. Which animal do you think might eat the most? Why?

______________________________________________

**Solve.**

7. Mrs. Torres' class went to school for 20 days in November.
They will go to school for 14 days in December..
How many more days did the children attend school in November than in December? _____ more days

# MONTHLY ASSESSMENT

**Color all the shapes with 4 equal sides red.**

1.

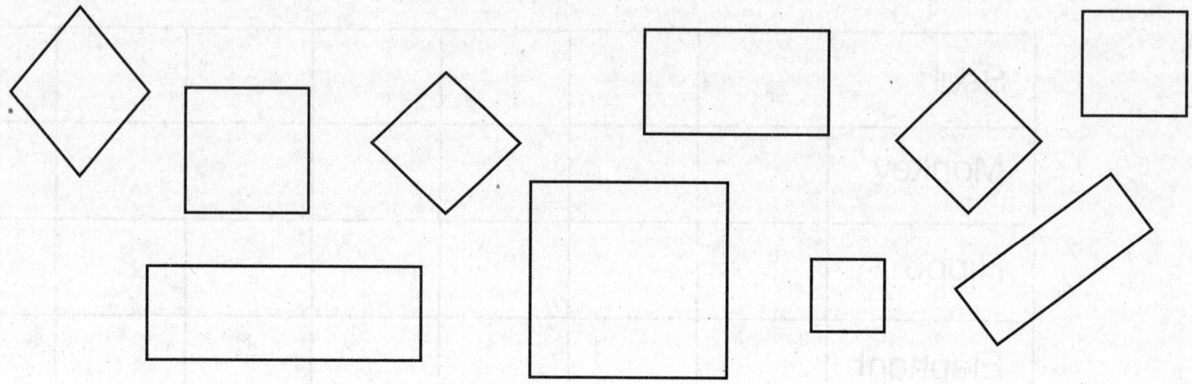

2. Draw three kinds of rectangles.

3. What makes squares different from rectangles?

______________________________________________

**Complete.**

| | You spend | You pay | Your change is |
|---|---|---|---|
| 4. | $.38 |  | ______¢ or $0.12 |
| 5. | $.45 |  | ______¢ or $0.00 |
| 6. | $.15 |  | ______¢ or $0.10 |
| 7. | $.95 |  | ______¢ or $0.05 |

# DAY 1 JANUARY

**Say the double. Add one more dot to make the double + 1. Write each sum.**

1. 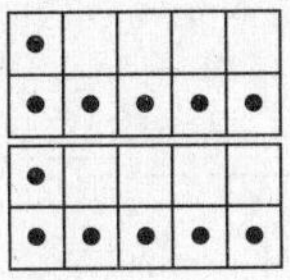

$$\begin{array}{r} 6 \\ +\ 6 \\ \hline \end{array} \qquad \begin{array}{r} 7 \\ +\ 6 \\ \hline \end{array}$$

2. 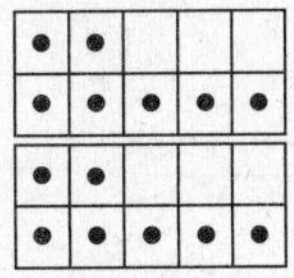

$$\begin{array}{r} 7 \\ +\ 7 \\ \hline \end{array} \qquad \begin{array}{r} 7 \\ +\ 8 \\ \hline \end{array}$$

3. 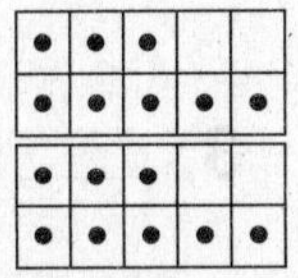

$$\begin{array}{r} 8 \\ +\ 8 \\ \hline \end{array} \qquad \begin{array}{r} 9 \\ +\ 8 \\ \hline \end{array}$$

**Continue the patterns.**

4. 2, 4, 6, 8, 10, 12, ____, ____, ____, ____

5. 1, 3, 5, 7, 9, 11, ____, ____, ____, ____

6.

|  |  |  |  |  |  | ____ | ____ | ____ |
|---|---|---|---|---|---|---|---|---|
| A | B | C | A | B | C | ____ | ____ | ____ |

# DAY 2

**Add a bundle of ten to each picture. Write the new number.**

1. 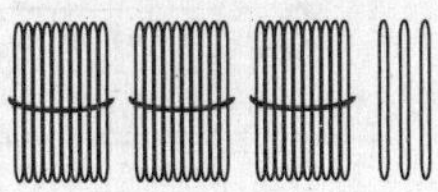

33 ____

2. 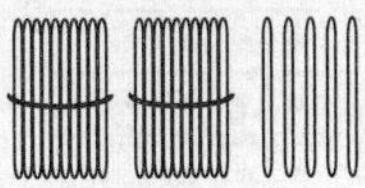

25 ____

3. 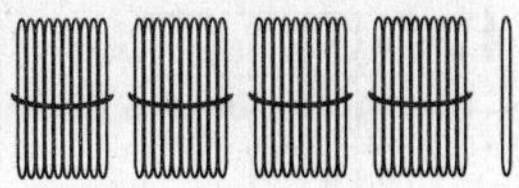

41 ____

4. 28 + 10 = ____ 5. 57 + 10 = ____ 6. 18 + 10 = ____

**Circle the fewest coins you need to buy each item.**

7. 

8. 

# DAY 3

**List the doubles from 6 + 6 to 9 + 9.**

1. 6 + 6 = ____ 2. ____ + ____ = ____

3. ____ + ____ = ____ 4. ____ + ____ = ____

**Write the double that comes before the double + 1.**

5. □ + □    5 + 6 = 11

6. □ + □    8 + 9 = 17

7. □ + □    8 + 7 = 15

**Draw an X on each figure with 4 square corners.**

8. 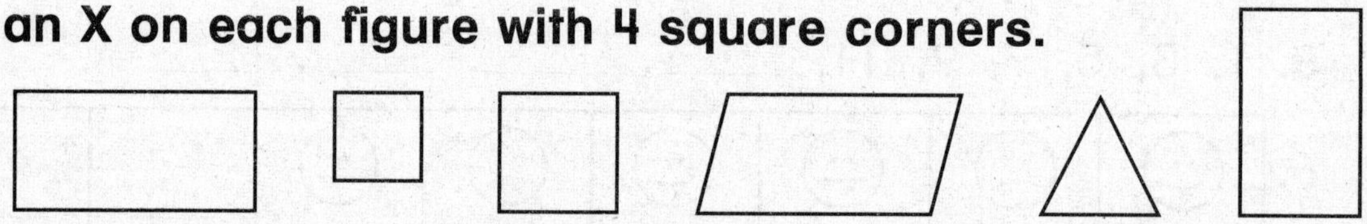

# DAY 4

**Write a subtraction fact to go with the double.**

1. 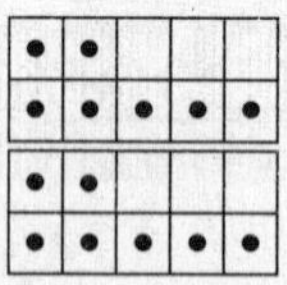 □ − □

2. 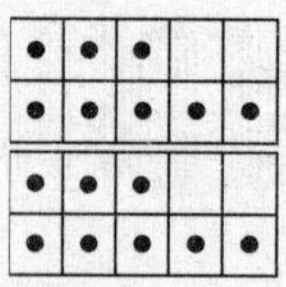 □ − □

3. 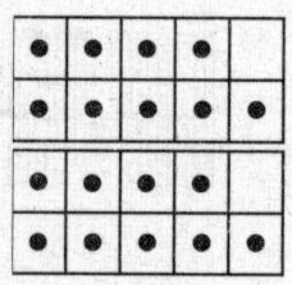 □ − □

4. 10 − 5 = ____ 5. 20 − 10 = ____ 6. 12 − 6 = ____

**Solve. Write the number sentence.**

7. Marcus tossed a penny 14 times. It came up  7 times.

How many times did it come up  ? ____________ times

# Day 5

**Write the double + 1 that goes with each double.**

1. $\begin{array}{r} 6 \\ +6 \\ \hline 12 \end{array}$ $\quad \begin{array}{r} \square \\ +\square \\ \hline \end{array}$

2. $\begin{array}{r} 8 \\ +8 \\ \hline 16 \end{array}$ $\quad \begin{array}{r} \square \\ +\square \\ \hline \end{array}$

3. $\begin{array}{r} 7 \\ +7 \\ \hline 14 \end{array}$ $\quad \begin{array}{r} \square \\ +\square \\ \hline \end{array}$

4. $\begin{array}{r} 5 \\ +5 \\ \hline 10 \end{array}$ $\quad \begin{array}{r} \square \\ +\square \\ \hline \end{array}$

**Subtract.**

5. 13 − 7 = ____  6. 16 − 8 = ____  7. 15 − 7 = ____

**Solve.**

8. You want to buy 2 pencils for 10¢ each at the school store. You have 2 quarters. How many will you use to buy the pencils? ______ quarter

# Day 6

**Add dots to each 10 frame to make a fast 10. Then draw any extra dots.**

1. 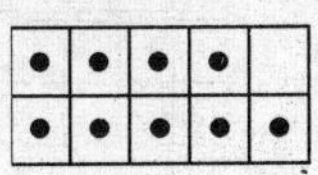

9 + 4 = ____

2. 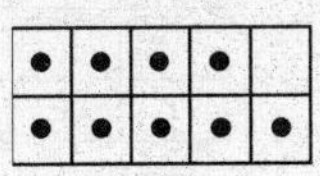

9 + 5 = ____

3. 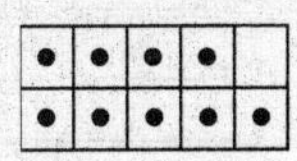

9 + 7 = ____

**Complete the pattern.**

4. □ △ □ △ ○ □ △ □ △ ○

# DAY 7

**Add 10. Write the new number.**

1. 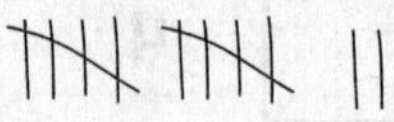
12 ____

2. 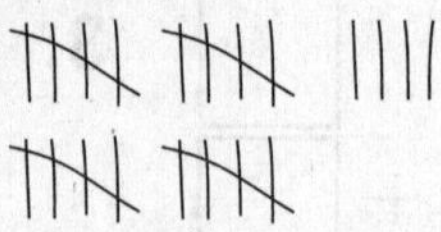
24 ____

3. 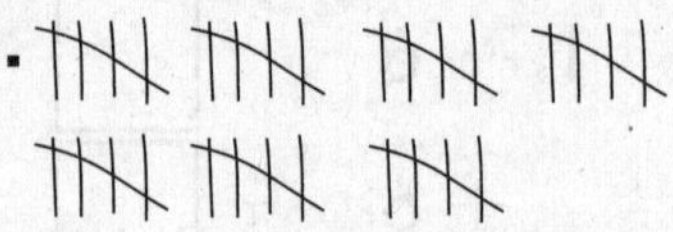
35 ____

**Add.**

4. 52 + 10 = ____
5. 44 + 10 = ____
6. 15 + 10 = ____

**Write the time.**

7. 

☐:☐☐ A.M.

8. 

☐☐:☐☐ A.M.

9. 

☐:☐☐ A.M.

# DAY 8

**Add dots to make a fast 10. Write how many all together.**

1. 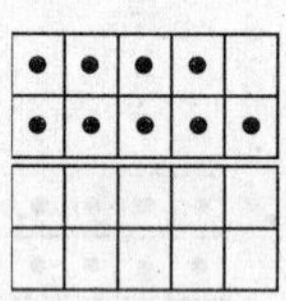
9
+ 6
____

2. 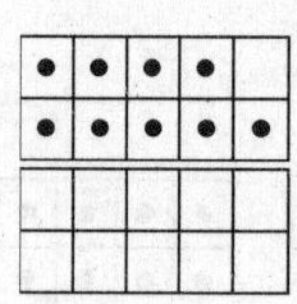
9
+ 3
____

3. 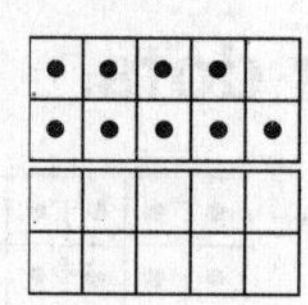
9
+ 7
____

4. 10 + 5 = ____
5. 10 + 2 = ____
6. 10 + 6 = ____

**Draw an X on each rectangle below. (Hint: There are more than 2.)**

7. 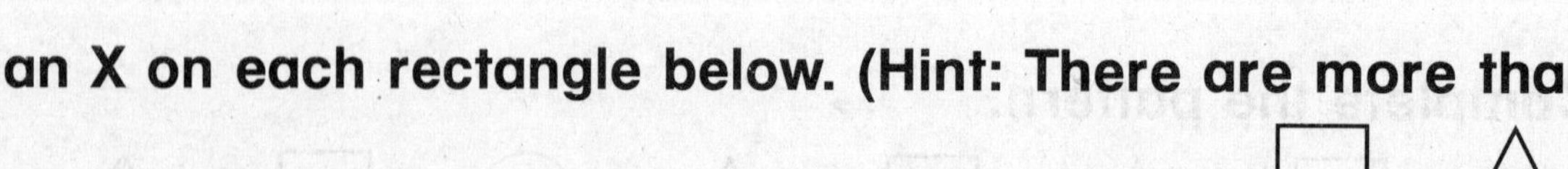

8. **What makes all squares rectangles?** ____________________

____________________________________________

# Day 9

**Add. Make a fast 10.**

1. $9 + 4 =$ ______  2. $9 + 6 =$ ______  3. $9 + 8 =$ ______

4. $9 + 3 =$ ______  5. $9 + 5 =$ ______  6. $9 + 7 =$ ______

7. Which fact above is also a double $+ 1$? ______

**Solve.**

8. Vinh has been in our class 8 more days than Lisa. Lisa has come 68 days. How many days has Vinh been in our class? ______

   Show how you got your answer. ______

# Day 10 CHECKPOINT

**Can you make another group of 10? Loop 10 beans. Write the total.**

1. 

   ______ ______

2. 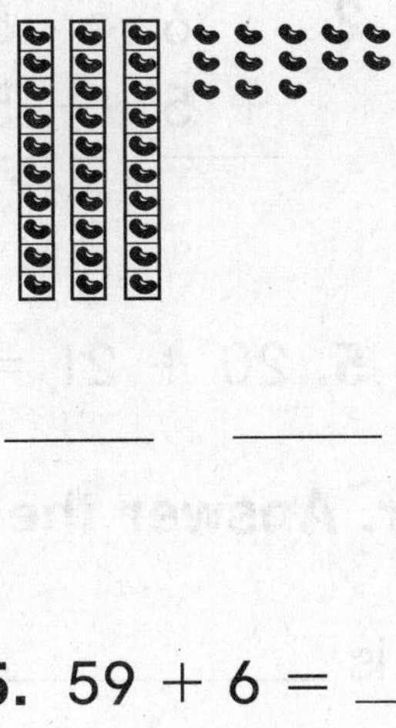

   ______ ______

3. 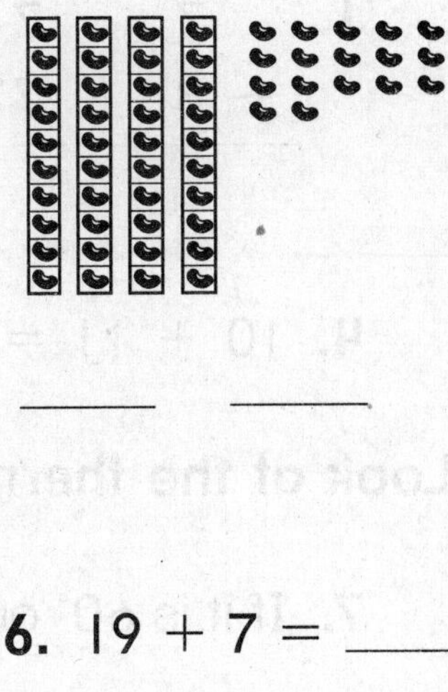

   ______ ______

**Add.**

4. $39 + 8 =$ ______  5. $59 + 6 =$ ______  6. $19 + 7 =$ ______

7. In problems 4, 5, and 6 above, how could you find each sum without counting? ______

______

# DAY 11

**Add. Make a fast 10 if you can.**

1. 35 + 8 = _____  2. 15 + 8 = _____  3. 45 + 8 = _____

4. 85 + 8 = _____  5. 65 + 8 = _____  6. 75 + 8 = _____

**Continue the pattern.**

7. 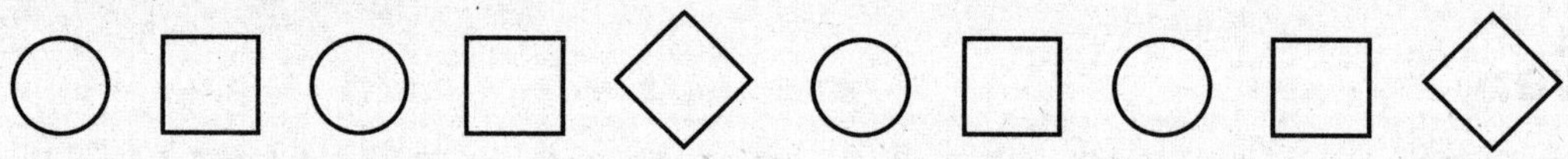

_____ _____ _____ _____ _____

# DAY 12

**Add.**

1. $\begin{array}{r} 7 \\ +\ 8 \\ \hline \end{array}$ $\begin{array}{r} 7 \\ +\ 7 \\ \hline \end{array}$  2. $\begin{array}{r} 6 \\ +\ 5 \\ \hline \end{array}$ $\begin{array}{r} 5 \\ +\ 5 \\ \hline \end{array}$  3. $\begin{array}{r} 6 \\ +\ 7 \\ \hline \end{array}$ $\begin{array}{r} 6 \\ +\ 6 \\ \hline \end{array}$

4. 10 + 11 = _____  5. 20 + 21 = _____  6. 30 + 31 = _____

**Look at the thermometer. Answer the questions.**

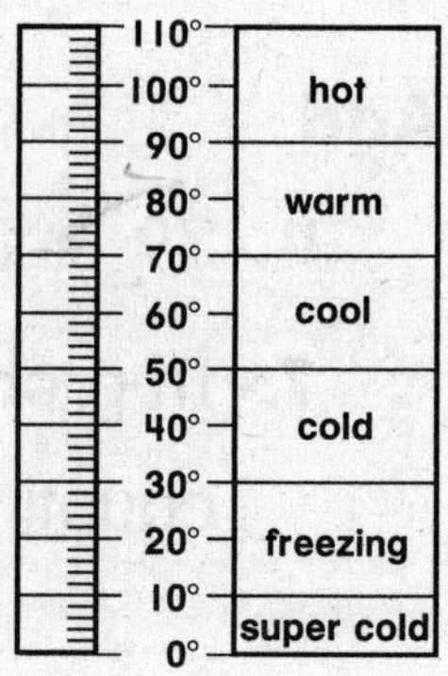


7. If it is 60° outside, it is __________.

8. If it is 15° outside, it is __________.

# DAY 13

**Add. Make a fast 10.**

1. 6 + 8 = ____
2. 76 + 8 = ____
3. 16 + 8 = ____
4. 26 + 8 = ____
5. 56 + 8 = ____
6. 36 + 8 = ____
7. 86 + 8 = ____
8. 66 + 8 = ____
9. 46 + 8 = ____

**Draw an X on each rhombus below.**

10. 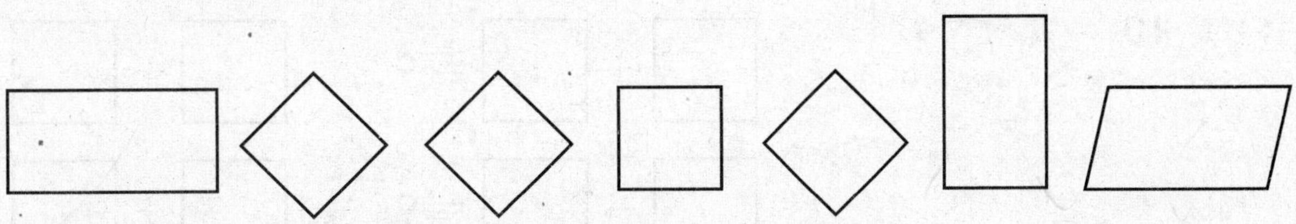

# DAY 14

**Add.**

| 1. | 2. | 3. | 4. | 5. |
|---|---|---|---|---|
| 7 + 9 | 8 + 7 | 6 + 8 | 8 + 9 | 9 + 6 |

| 6. | 7. | 8. | 9. | 10. |
|---|---|---|---|---|
| 9 + 9 | 5 + 9 | 7 + 8 | 8 + 8 | 9 + 8 |

**Solve.**

11. Marina collected 9 stickers.
Andrew gave her 7 more.
How many stickers does she have? ______ stickers

# DAY 15

**Add. Make a fast 10.**

1. 17 + 8 = ____ 2. 87 + 8 = ____ 3. 7 + 8 = ____

4. 27 + 8 = ____ 5. 57 + 8 = ____ 6. 37 + 8 = ____

7. 77 + 8 = ____ 8. 67 + 8 = ____ 9. 47 + 8 = ____

**Record 4 ways you can divide 9 pennies between 2 piggy banks.**

10. 

☐ + ☐ = 9 ☐ + ☐ = 9

☐ + ☐ = 9 ☐ + ☐ = 9

# DAY 16

**Add.**

1. 58 + 8 = ____ 2. 18 + 8 = ____ 3. 68 + 8 = ____

4. 38 + 8 = ____ 5. 78 + 8 = ____ 6. 48 + 8 = ____

**Continue the pattern. Draw the clock hands to show the time.**

7. 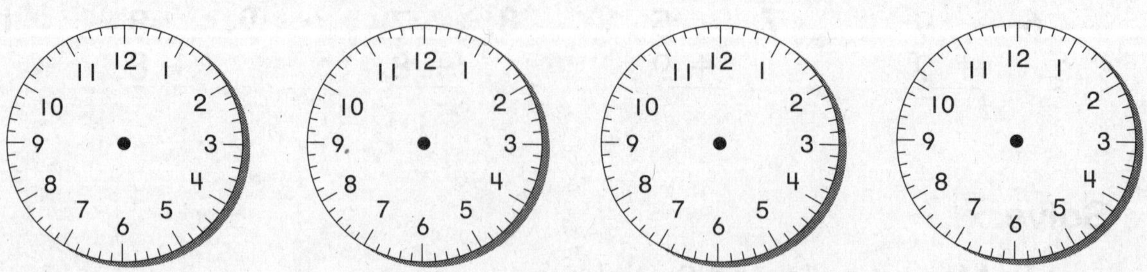

6:00 A.M. 9:00 A.M. 12:00 noon ___:___ P.M.

# DAY 17

**Add.**

**1.** 19 + 8 **2.** 49 + 8 **3.** 29 + 8 **4.** 79 + 8 **5.** 59 + 8 **6.** 39 + 8

**Look at the thermometers.**
**Record the temperatures.**
**Write <, >, or =.**

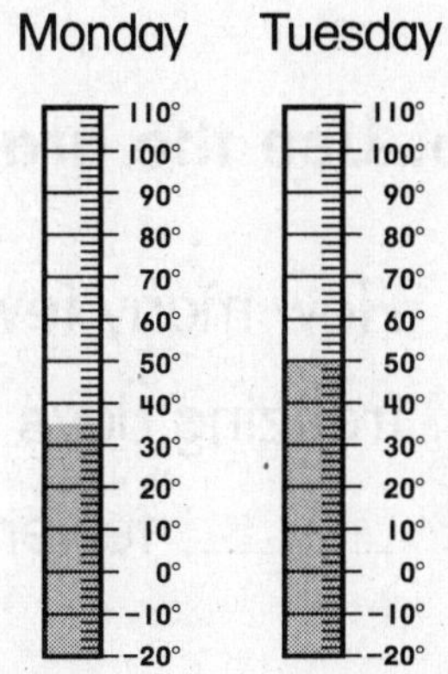


**7.** ______ ◯ ______
Monday Tuesday

# DAY 18

**Subtract. (Hint: Count up to 10 and then add the extras.)**

**1.** 15 − 9 **2.** 15 − 7 **3.** 17 − 8 **4.** 18 − 9 **5.** 16 − 7 **6.** 16 − 9

**Circle the shapes that show a line of symmetry.**

**7.**

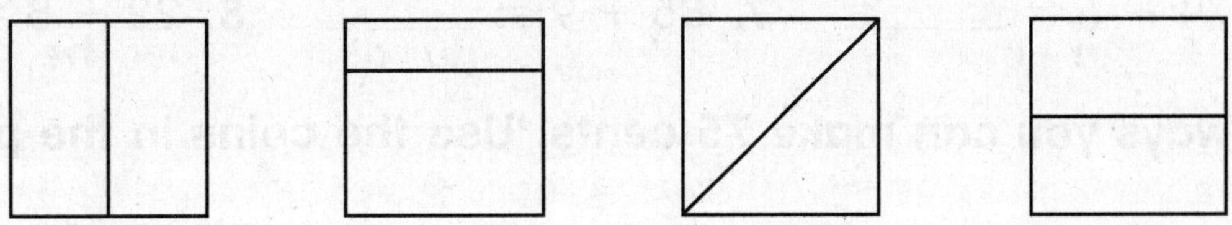

**8.**

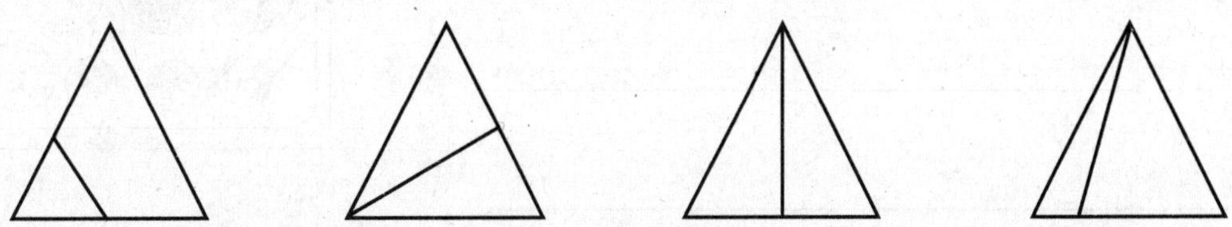

# DAY 19

**Add.**

| 1. | 2. | 3. | 4. | 5. | 6. |
|---|---|---|---|---|---|
| $5 + 9$ | $6 + 7$ | $8 + 7$ | $9 + 7$ | $6 + 8$ | $8 + 9$ |

**Solve. Use the graph.**

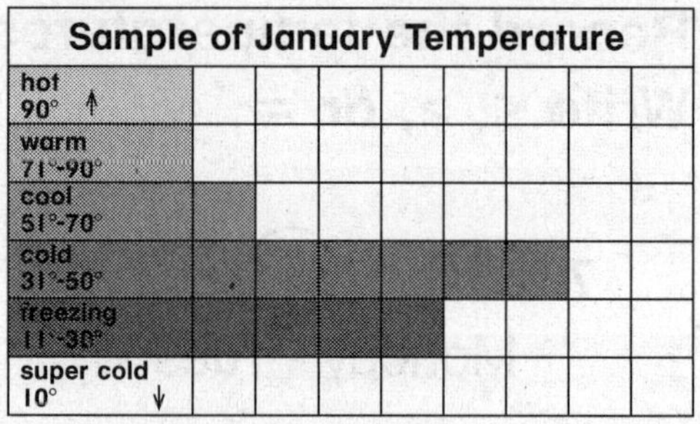


7. How many fewer cool days than freezing days are on the graph?

_______ fewer cool days

# DAY 20

**Add. Make a fast 10 when you can.**

| 1. | 2. | 3. | 4. | 5. |
|---|---|---|---|---|
| $38 + 8$ | $49 + 6$ | $52 + 9$ | $63 + 5$ | $97 + 2$ |

6. $74 + 6 =$ _______ 7. $85 + 9 =$ _______ 8. $22 + 8 =$ _______

**List 3 ways you can make 75 cents. Use the coins in the purse.**

9. ______________________________

10. ______________________________

11. ______________________________

# MONTHLY ASSESSMENT

**Use the Calendar.**

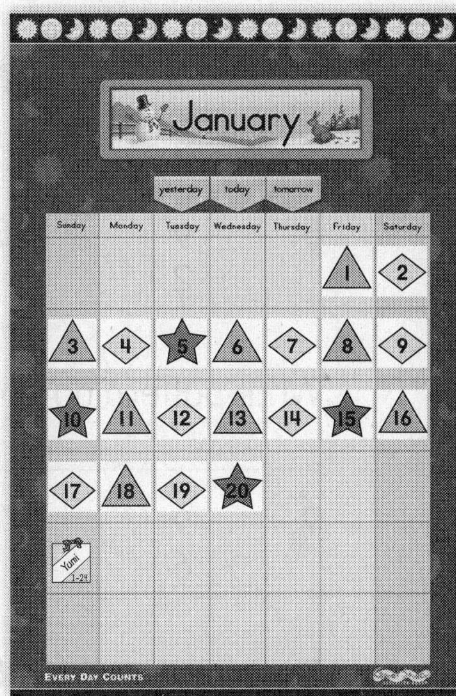


1. Write the name of the month.

   ____________________

2. Why is it a special month?

   ______________________________________

3. What is the last month of the year?

   ____________________

4. Describe the pattern of shapes.

   ______________________________________

   ______________________________________

5. What shape is January 20th? ____________________

6. What other dates have stars? ____________________

7. What date do you think the next star will be on? ______

   How do you know? ______________________________________

8. Draw a line of symmetry on each of these figures.

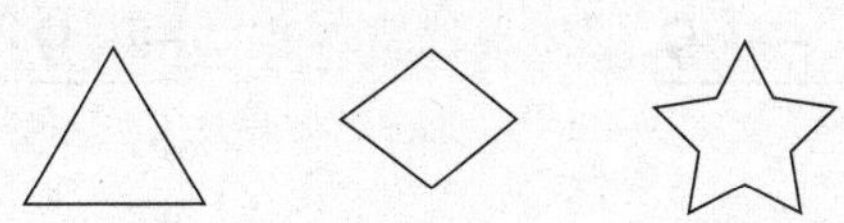

9. What is a line of symmetry? ______________________________________

   ______________________________________

# MONTHLY ASSESSMENT

**Add.**

| | | | |
|---|---|---|---|
| **1.** 9 + 6 | **2.** 9 + 9 | **3.** 9 + 7 | **4.** 9 + 4 |
| **5.** 9 + 2 | **6.** 9 + 5 | **7.** 9 + 8 | **8.** 9 + 3 |

What pattern do you see? ______________________________

______________________________

| | | | |
|---|---|---|---|
| **9.** 9 + 6 | **10.** 19 + 6 | **11.** 29 + 6 | **12.** 9 + 8 |
| **13.** 19 + 8 | **14.** 29 + 8 | **15.** 9 + 7 | **16.** 19 + 7 |

**Subtract.**

| | | | |
|---|---|---|---|
| **17.** 15 − 7 | **18.** 17 − 8 | **19.** 3 − 1 | **20.** 7 − 3 |
| **21.** 9 − 4 | **22.** 11 − 5 | **23.** 13 − 6 | **24.** 5 − 2 |
| **25.** 18 − 9 | **26.** 12 − 9 | **27.** 11 − 9 | **28.** 20 − 9 |
| **29.** 19 − 9 | **30.** 17 − 9 | **31.** 16 − 9 | **32.** 14 − 9 |

# MONTHLY ASSESSMENT

**Use the graph to answer the questions.**

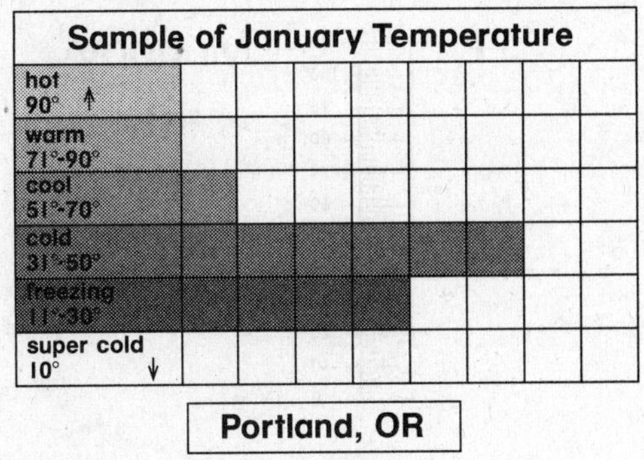


1. What month does the graph show?

   ____________________

2. How many days were recorded?

   _______

3. Was the weather ever super cold this month? _______

4. How many more days was it cold than cool? _______

5. What was the temperature for most of the days? ______________

**Solve.**

6. Amber and Charlie went to the carnival. They each bought 18 tickets for rides. Amber spent 8 tickets on the Ferris wheel. How many tickets did she have left? _______ tickets

   Explain your strategy. ________________________________________

   ________________________________________________________

7. Charlie spent 2 more tickets than Amber. How many tickets did he spend? _______

   How many tickets did he have left? _______

8. At 10 A.M. the temperature is 25°. By 2:30 P.M., it has gone up 20°. What is the temperature at 2:30? ____________

# MONTHLY ASSESSMENT

**Shade in the temperatures.**

1. 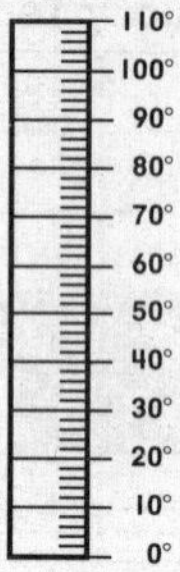
Monday
40°

2. 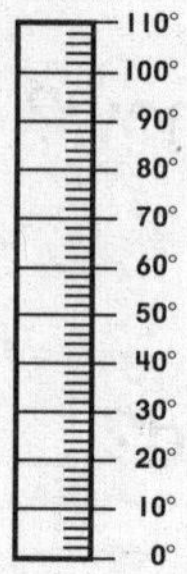
Tuesday
20 degrees warmer

3. 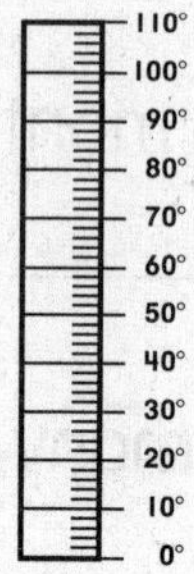
Wednesday
10° cooler than Monday

**Write the times. Draw the hands on the clocks.**

4. 
I get up at ______.

5. 
I watch TV at ______.

6. 
I go to bed at ______.

**Mark the coins you need.**

7. 

8. 
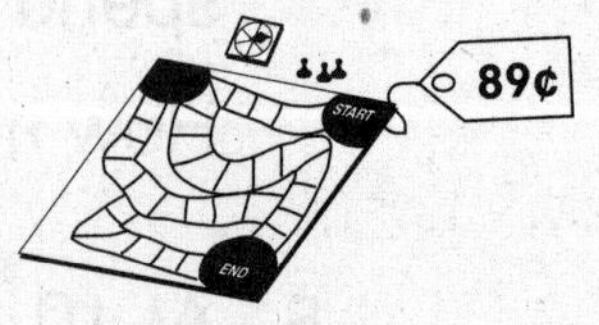


9. 

# DAY 1 FEBRUARY

**Write the numbers. Add.**

1. 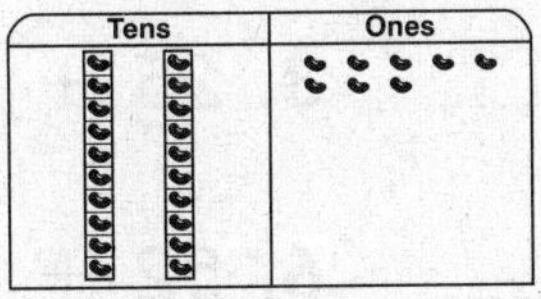

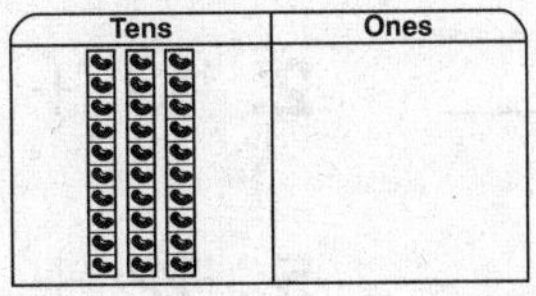

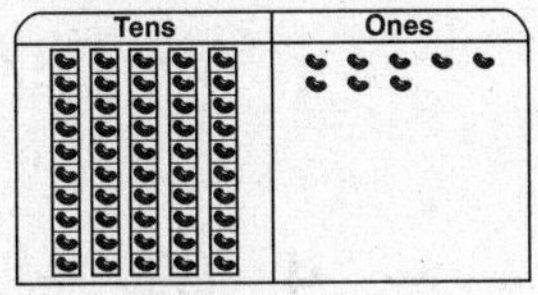


_______ + _______ = _______

2. 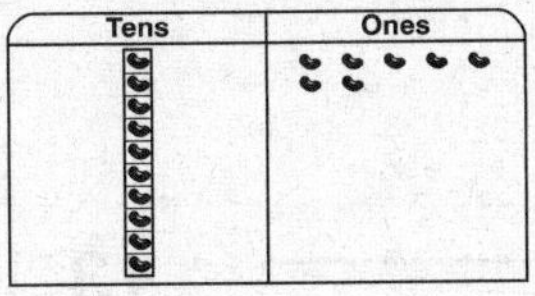

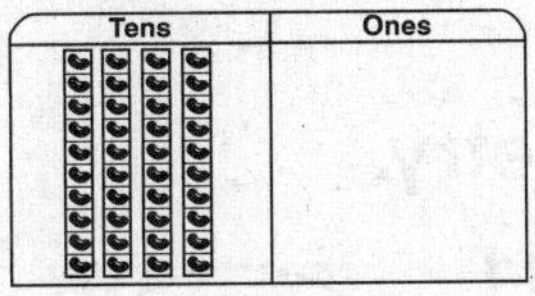

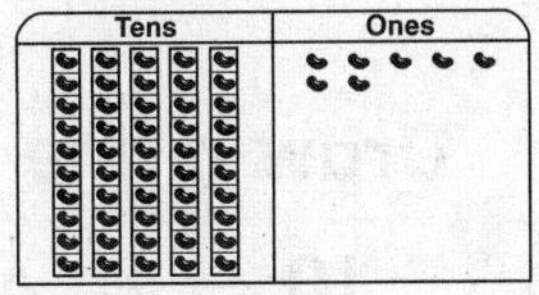


_______ + _______ = _______

**Complete the pattern and count. Write how much.**

3. 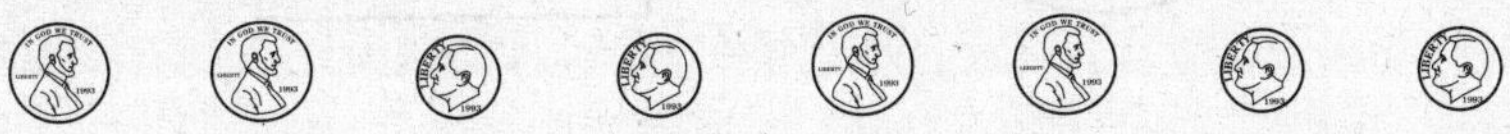

A A B B A A B B ___ ___ ___ ___

_______ ¢

# DAY 2

**Write the numbers. Add.**

1. 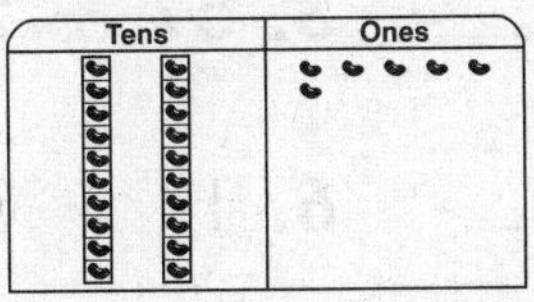

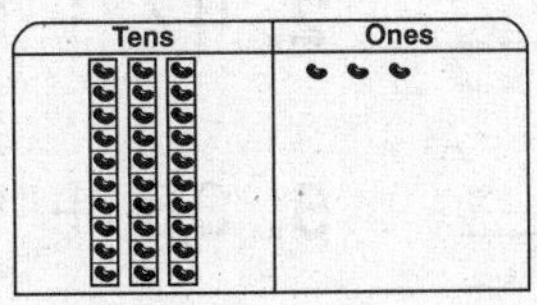

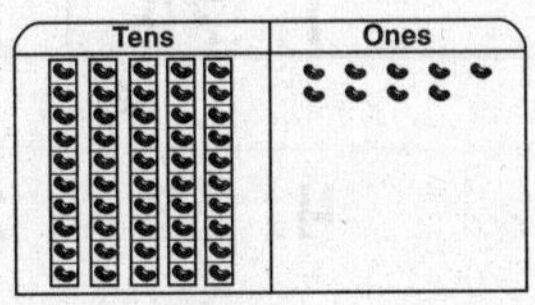


_______ + _______ = _______

**Use the thermometer to answer the questions.**

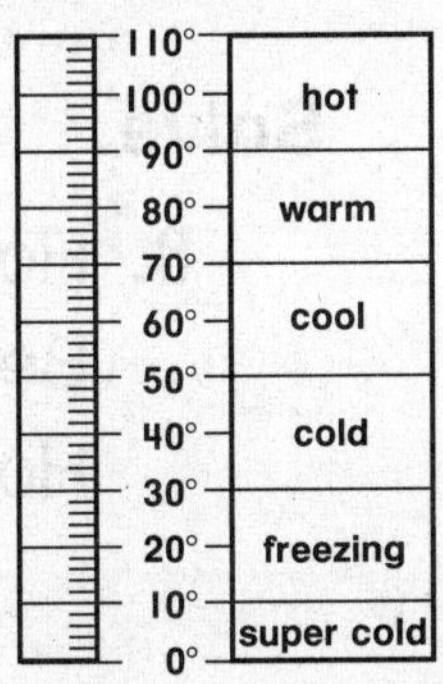


2. If it is 80° outside, can you go swimming? _______

3. If it is 35° outside, is it hot or cold? _______

# DAY 3

**Add. You may use beans and beansticks and a tens and ones mat.**

1. 57 + 22 = ____ 2. 43 + 56 = ____ 3. 25 + 3 = ____

4. 37 + 32 = ____ 5. 42 + 24 = ____ 6. 52 + 24 = ____

7. 66 + 30 = ____ 8. 87 + 12 = ____ 9. 40 + 35 = ____

**Draw a line of symmetry.**

10. 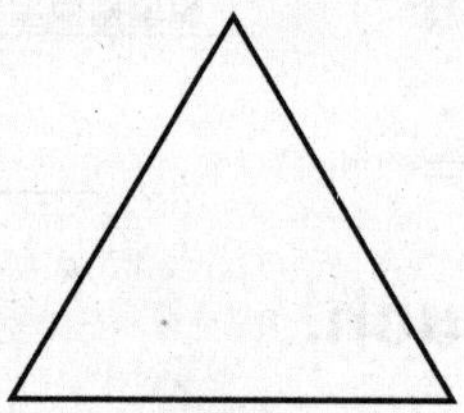

11. 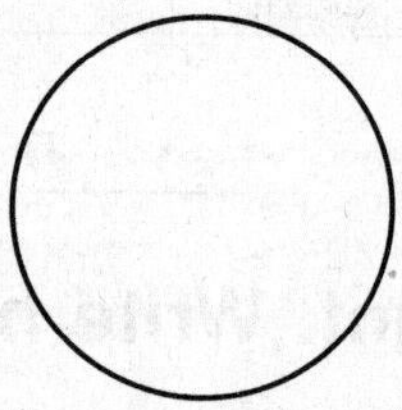

12. 

13. 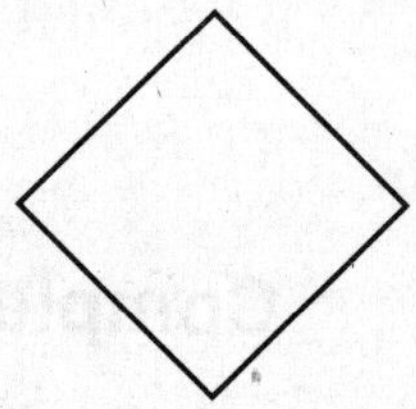

# DAY 4

**Add. You may use beansticks and beans.**

1. 74 + 20 = ____ 2. 47 + 30 = ____ 3. 57 + 21 = ____

4. 63 + 25 = ____ 5. 38 + 41 = ____ 6. 14 + 80 = ____

7. What strategy did you use? ________________________

**Solve.**

8. Raul had 48 cents in his pocket.
Beata gave him 4 dimes.
How much money does he have now? ______¢

# DAY 5

**Add.**

| **1.** | **2.** | **3.** | **4.** | **5.** | **6.** | **7.** |
|---|---|---|---|---|---|---|
| 45 | 16 | 59 | 68 | 47 | 82 | 88 |
| + 50 | + 40 | + 30 | + 20 | + 20 | + 10 | + 10 |

**8.** What do you notice about adding groups of 10 to a number?

______________________________________________

______________________________________________

**Write the largest number you can. Circle the tens.**

**9.** 4, 9, 3 ______ **10.** 5, 6, 8 ______ **11.** 3, 4, 6 ______ **12.** 5, 8, 7 ______ **13.** 7, 1, 8 ______

# DAY 6

**Add.**

**1.** 13 + 80 = ______ **2.** 40 + 60 = ______ **3.** 59 + 40 = ______

**4.** 57 + 30 = ______ **5.** 25 + 70 = ______ **6.** 25 + 50 = ______

**Complete the pattern. Count the money.**

**7.** 

______¢

**8.** 

______¢

**9.** 

______¢

**10.** 

______¢

# DAY 7

**Add.**

1. 67 + 32 = ____ 2. 57 + 32 = ____ 3. 68 + 21 = ____

4. 47 + 52 = ____ 5. 54 + 35 = ____ 6. 83 + 16 = ____

7. 74 + 11 = ____ 8. 72 + 27 = ____ 9. 22 + 42 = ____

**Read the temperatures.**

10. Circle the thermometer that shows the warmest temperature. Draw an X on the thermometer that shows the coolest temperature.

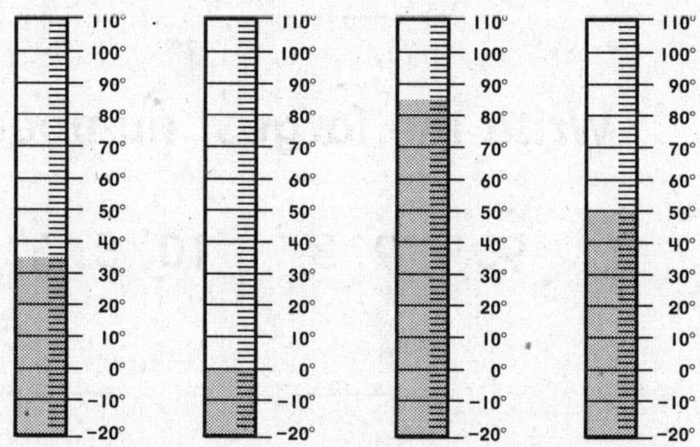


# DAY 8

**Add.**

1. 78 + 20 = ____ 2. 34 + 51 = ____ 3. 85 + 14 = ____

4. 63 + 24 = ____ 5. 15 + 70 = ____ 6. 28 + 60 = ____

7. 45 + 54 = ____ 8. 33 + 62 = ____ 9. 50 + 49 = ____

**Write < or >.**

10. 487 ◯ 329 11. 986 ◯ 896 12. 346 ◯ 423 13. 785 ◯ 857

14. How did you know which number was larger? ______________________

______________________________________________

# DAY 9

**Add.**

1. 53 + 35 = ____
2. 16 + 61 = ____
3. 23 + 32 = ____
4. 31 + 13 = ____
5. 42 + 24 = ____
6. 34 + 43 = ____
7. 54 + 45 = ____
8. 25 + 52 = ____
9. What pattern do you see? ________________________________

________________________________________________

**Solve.**

10. Tim has collected 13 rocks.
    Sandra has collected 31 rocks.
    How many rocks have they collected? ____ rocks

# DAY 10 CHECKPOINT

**Add.**
**Circle the sums that were easiest to find.**

1. 24 + 13 = ____
2. 82 + 10 = ____
3. 78 + 20 = ____
4. 70 + 14 = ____
5. 62 + 17 = ____
6. 43 + 50 = ____
7. 18 + 30 = ____
8. 76 + 12 = ____
9. 20 + 52 = ____

**Draw a line of symmetry.**

10. 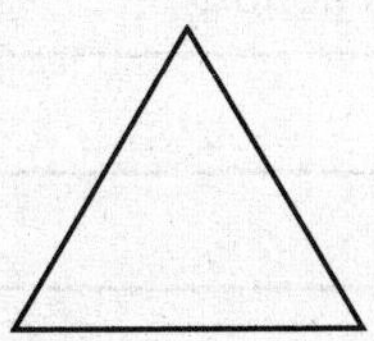

11. 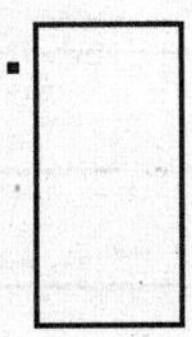

12. 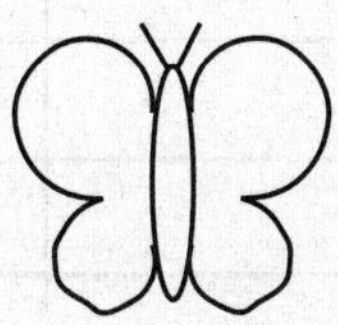

13. 

# DAY 11

**Add.**

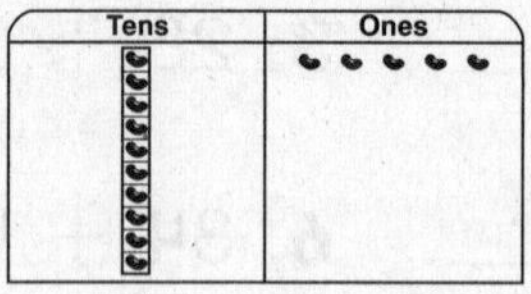

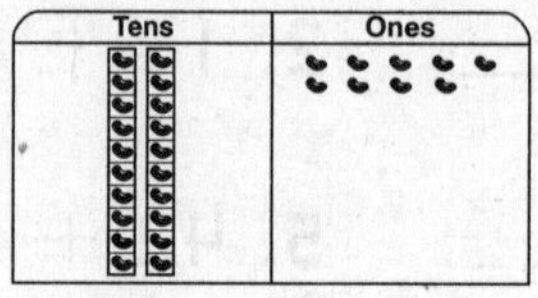

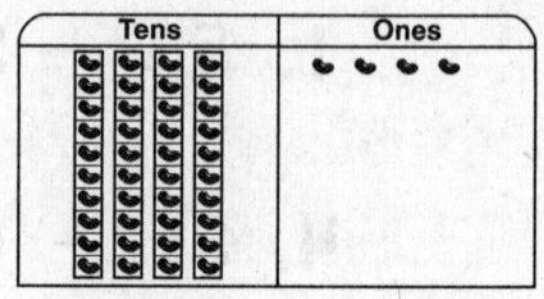


1. ______ + ______ = ______

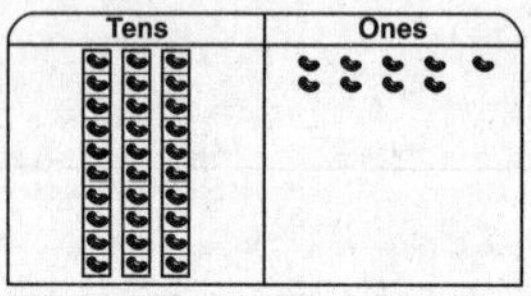

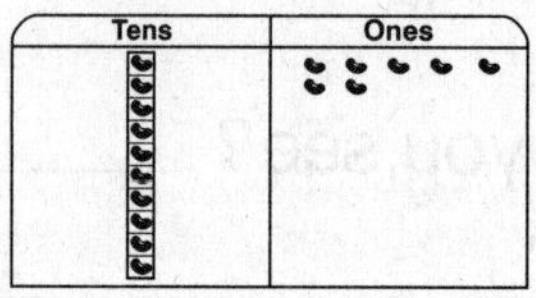

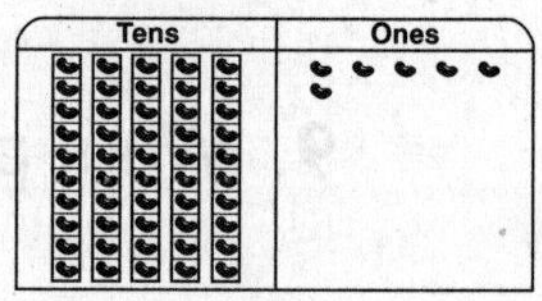


2. ______ + ______ = ______

3. Did you need to regroup? ______

**Complete the pattern.**

4. 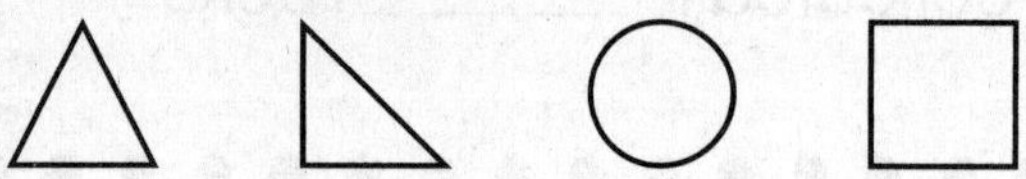 ______ ______ ______ ______

# DAY 12

**Add. Circle the problems you regrouped.**

| 1. | 2. | 3. | 4. | 5. | 6. | 7. |
|---|---|---|---|---|---|---|
| 46 | 74 | 28 | 64 | 39 | 28 | 84 |
| + 33 | + 28 | + 16 | + 29 | + 10 | + 25 | + 14 |

**Show 3 ways to make a dollar.**

| | Ways to Make $1.00 | | |
|---|---|---|---|
| | Quarters | Dimes | Nickels |
| 8. | | | |
| 9. | | | |
| 10. | | | |

# DAY 13

**Add. You may use beansticks.**

| | | | |
|---|---|---|---|
| 1. 23 + 57 | 2. 34 + 68 | 3. 45 + 37 | 4. 56 + 37 |
| 5. 67 + 39 | 6. 78 + 43 | 7. 89 + 32 | 8. 90 + 10 |

9. When do you have to regroup? ______________________________

______________________________________________

**Draw lines to match the halves.**

10.

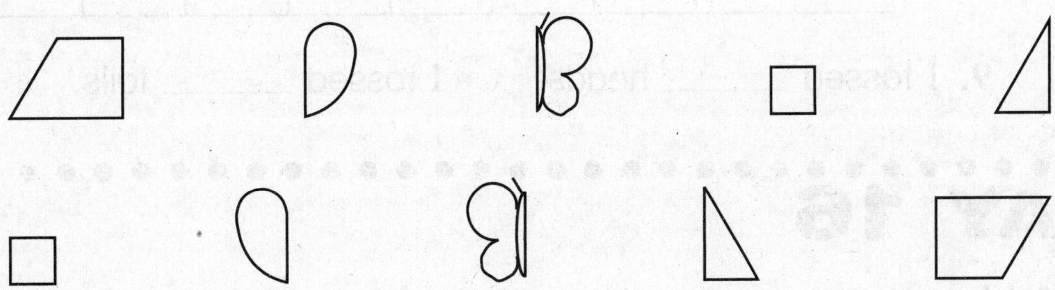

# DAY 14

**Add. You may use beansticks.**

| | | | |
|---|---|---|---|
| 1. 23 + 17 | 2. 46 + 65 | 3. 52 + 47 | 4. 85 + 28 |
| 5. 94 + 76 | 6. 79 + 54 | 7. 93 + 58 | 8. 28 + 74 |

**Solve.**

9. Soo recycles newspapers. Last week, she recycled 24 pounds of newspapers. This week, she recycled 28 pounds of newspapers. How many pounds has she recycled? ______ pounds

# DAY 15

**Add.**

1. 15 + 15 =
2. 25 + 25 =
3. 35 + 35 =
4. 45 + 45 =
5. 55 + 55 =
6. 65 + 65 =
7. 75 + 75 =

**Toss a penny 10 times. Graph the results.**

8.

| Penny Toss | | | | | | | | | | |
|---|---|---|---|---|---|---|---|---|---|---|
|  | | | | | | | | | | |
|  | | | | | | | | | | |

9. I tossed ______ heads. I tossed ______ tails.

# DAY 16

**Add.**
**Circle the problems you regrouped.**

1. 38 + 18 =
2. 39 + 19 =
3. 40 + 20 =
4. 41 + 18 =
5. 42 + 19 =
6. 43 + 20 =
7. 44 + 18 =

8. If there is a 0 in the ones place in one of the addends, will you have to regroup? Explain. ______________________________
______________________________

**Complete the number patterns.**

9. 328, 428, 528, ______, ______, ______

10. 200, 400, 600, ______, ______

# DAY 17

**Add.**

| | | | | | | |
|---|---|---|---|---|---|---|
| **1.** 8 + 7 | **2.** 18 + 17 | **3.** 28 + 27 | **4.** 38 + 37 | **5.** 48 + 47 | **6.** 58 + 57 | **7.** 68 + 67 |

**8.** What pattern do you see? ______________________________

______________________________________________

______________________________________________

**Use a ruler. Estimate and then measure.**

| | Estimate | Measure |
|---|---|---|
| **9.** | My pencil is ______ in. | about ______ in. |
| **10.** | My foot is ______ in. | about ______ in. |
| **11.** | My scissors are ______ in. | about ______ in. |

# DAY 18

**Add these fast facts.**

| | | | | | | | |
|---|---|---|---|---|---|---|---|
| **1.** 8 + 8 | **2.** 9 + 9 | **3.** 10 + 8 | **4.** 11 + 9 | **5.** 12 + 8 | **6.** 13 + 7 | **7.** 14 + 4 | **8.** 15 + 3 |

**Circle the digit in the tens place.**

**9.** 343 867 254 198 367 976 643

**Circle the digit in the hundreds place.**

**10.** 487 573 978 307 823 796 821

# DAY 19

**Add. Regroup if you need to.**

| 1. | 2. | 3. | 4. | 5. | 6. | 7. |
|---|---|---|---|---|---|---|
| 78 + 18 | 29 + 19 | 36 + 26 | 72 + 22 | 84 + 14 | 63 + 23 | 37 + 17 |

8. How did knowing the doubles help you with these problems?

______________________________

______________________________

______________________________

**Solve.**

9. Two second grade classes are going to a play. There are 24 children in one of the classes. There are 19 children in the other class. How many children will go to the play? ______ children

# DAY 20

**Add.**

| 1. | 2. | 3. | 4. | 5. | 6. | 7. |
|---|---|---|---|---|---|---|
| 86 + 14 | 73 + 24 | 29 + 63 | 30 + 60 | 57 + 25 | 46 + 24 | 29 + 29 |

**Solve.**

8. Aaron has 7 coins in his pocket. There are pennies, nickels, dimes, and quarters. All the coins are not the same. What is the most money he could have? ______________________

9. What is the smallest amount he could have? ____________

______________________________

# MONTHLY ASSESSMENT

**Use the Calendar.**

1. Write the name of the month.

   ______________ How many days

   does this month have? ________

2. Abraham Lincoln's birthday is February 12. What day of the week will that be?

   ______________

3. Describe the pattern of shapes.

   ______________________________

4. Describe the pattern using letters. ____________________

5. Do both shapes have a line of symmetry? ________
   Draw a picture to prove your thinking.

6. The last day of February is the 28th. Is that number even or odd?

   How do you know? ______________________________

   ______________________________________________

7. Continue the pattern. What shape is 29?

   ______________

# MONTHLY ASSESSMENT

**Add. Use beansticks if you need them.**

1. 25 + 10 = ____ 2. 43 + 30 = ____ 3. 87 + 10 = ____

4. 46 + 40 = ____ 5. 25 + 50 = ____ 6. 68 + 30 = ____

**Add. Use beansticks if you need them.**

| 7. | 8. | 9. | 10. | 11. | 12. |
|---|---|---|---|---|---|
| 25 + 17 | 46 + 56 | 53 + 29 | 37 + 53 | 19 + 52 | 35 + 56 |

| 13. | 14. | 15. | 16. | 17. | 18. |
|---|---|---|---|---|---|
| 69 + 13 | 47 + 38 | 81 + 19 | 54 + 38 | 76 + 25 | 83 + 28 |

**Add. Will you regroup? Circle yes or no.**

| 19. | 20. | 21. | 22. |
|---|---|---|---|
| 43 + 18 | 59 + 21 | 88 + 40 | 53 + 16 |
| yes no | yes no | yes no | yes no |

23. I must regroup when ________________________________

________________________________________

**Circle the number in the tens place.**

24. 438 516 742 125 292 304

**Circle the number in the ones place.**

25. 627 152 413 986 378 864

# MONTHLY ASSESSMENT

**Solve.**

1. Imogene went to a garage sale. She wanted to buy a book for 45¢ and a notebook for 57¢. She had 78¢ in her pocket. Could she buy what she wanted? Explain your thinking.

   ______________________________________________

2. Fred wants to buy a boat for 68¢. He has 2 quarters, 1 dime, and 12 pennies.

   Can he buy the boat? ______________

3. There are 18 children in one second grade class. The other second grade class has 7 more children.

   How many children are in the class? ______ children

   How many children are in both classes? ______ children

4. Lanny has 3 quarters. She buys a book for 50¢ and a pencil for 14¢.

   How much change will she get back? ______¢

   If she gets 2 coins in change, what will they be? ______________

**Look at the penny toss graph.**

5. How many times was the penny tossed?

   ______ times

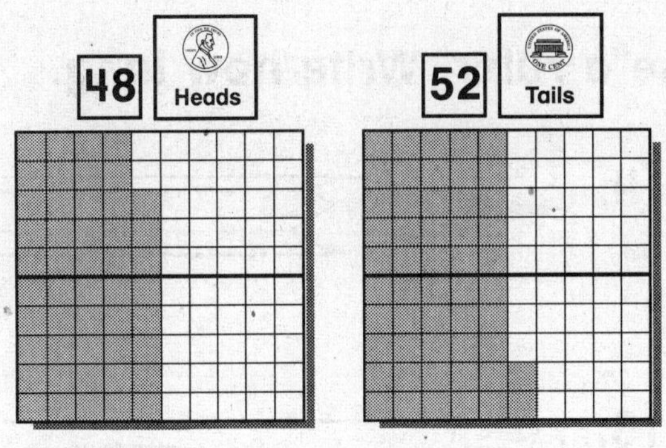

# MONTHLY ASSESSMENT

**Draw a line of symmetry.**

**1.** 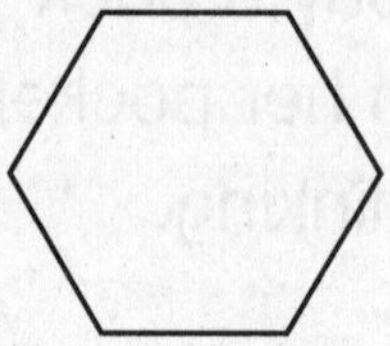

**2.** 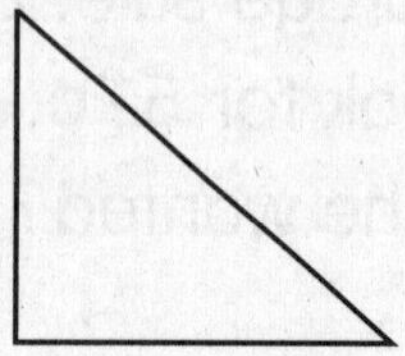

**3.** 

**Do the coins make a dollar? Write yes or no.**

| | Quarters | Dimes | Nickels | Pennies | yes or no |
|---|---|---|---|---|---|
| **4.** | 1 | 5 | 3 | 10 | |
| **5.** | 2 | 2 | 1 | 20 | |
| **6.** | 1 | 4 | 3 | 2 | |
| **7.** | | | | 100 | |
| **8.** | 4 | | | | |
| **9.** | | 8 | 2 | | |

**Color the temperatures on the thermometers.**

**10.** 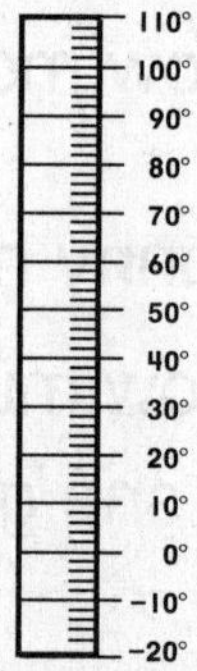


**11.** 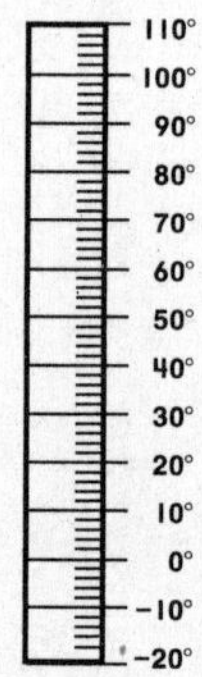


**10.** It is 30° outside.

**11.** It is 80° outside.

**12.** I can swim when it is ___________.

**13.** I can play in the snow when it is ___________.

**Use a ruler. Write how long.**

**14.** 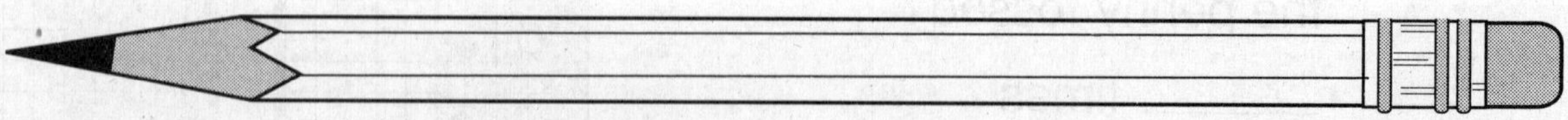

_________ inches

**15.** 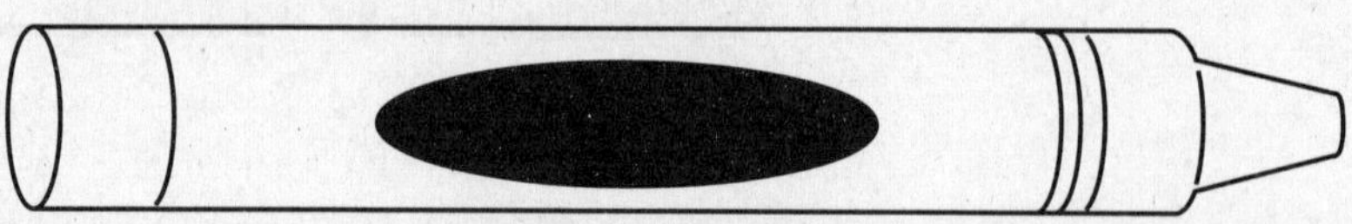

_________ inches

# DAY 1 MARCH

**Circle the problems with 10 or more ones. Add.**

1. $\begin{array}{r} 37 \\ +16 \\ \hline \end{array}$ 2. $\begin{array}{r} 52 \\ +16 \\ \hline \end{array}$ 3. $\begin{array}{r} 29 \\ +25 \\ \hline \end{array}$ 4. $\begin{array}{r} 28 \\ +37 \\ \hline \end{array}$ 5. $\begin{array}{r} 46 \\ +21 \\ \hline \end{array}$ 6. $\begin{array}{r} 74 \\ +23 \\ \hline \end{array}$

**Continue the pattern.**

7. 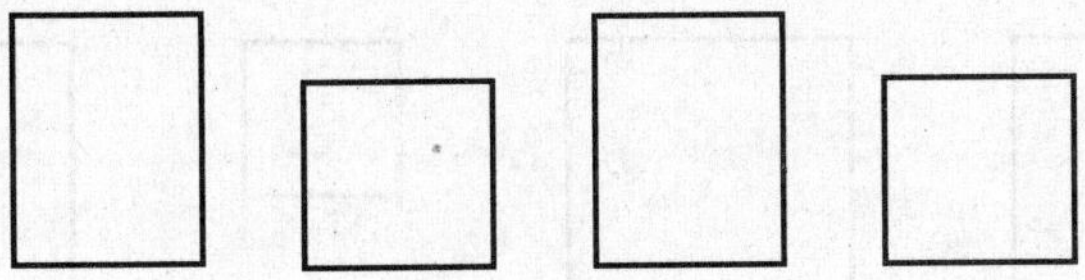 ____ ____ ____ ____

# DAY 2

**Circle the problems with 10 or more ones. Add.**

1. 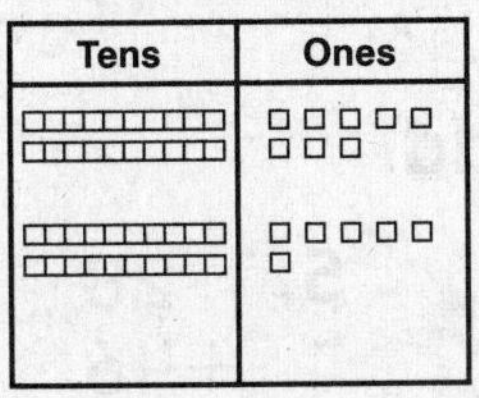

$\begin{array}{r} 28 \\ +26 \\ \hline \end{array}$

2. 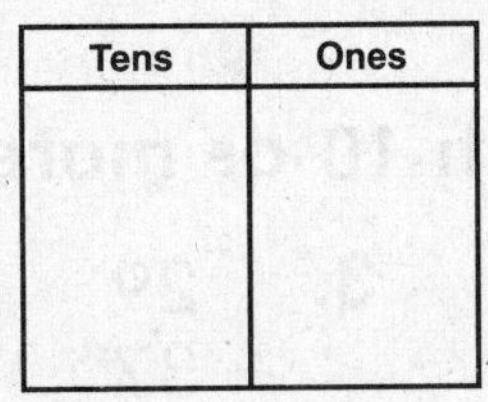

$\begin{array}{r} 31 \\ +23 \\ \hline \end{array}$

3. 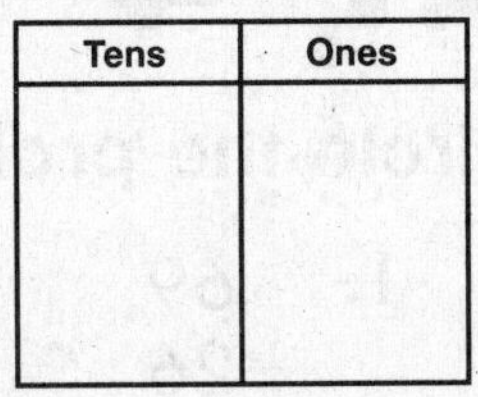

$\begin{array}{r} 49 \\ +27 \\ \hline \end{array}$

**Use a ruler. Estimate, then measure.**

4. 

Guess: ______________ inches Check: about ______ inches

5. 

Guess: ______________ inches Check: about ______ inches

# DAY 3

**Circle the problems with 10 or more ones. Add.**

| 1. | 2. | 3. | 4. | 5. | 6. |
|---|---|---|---|---|---|
| 63 | 49 | 28 | 58 | 57 | 80 |
| +21 | +36 | +47 | +21 | +25 | +19 |

**Color the same size rectangles blue.**
**Color the same size squares red.**

7.

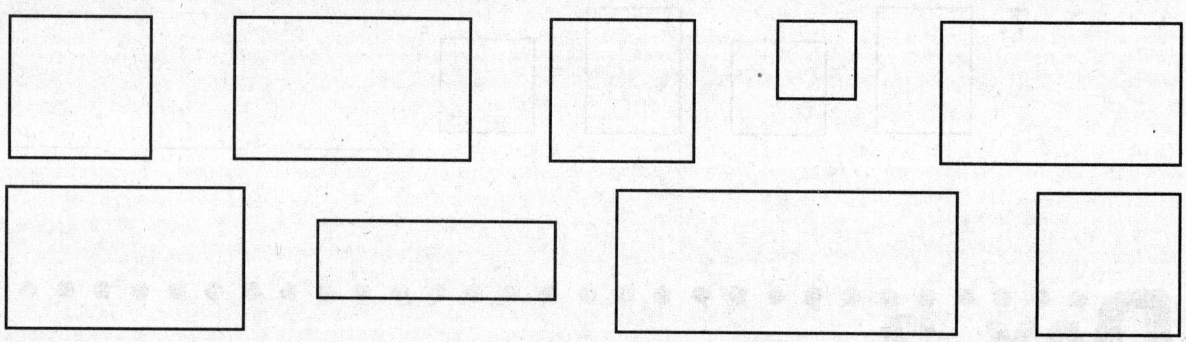

# DAY 4

**Circle the problems with 10 or more ones. Add.**

| 1. | 2. | 3. | 4. | 5. | 6. |
|---|---|---|---|---|---|
| 69 | 34 | 29 | 72 | 28 | 44 |
| +26 | +22 | +37 | +21 | +46 | +27 |

**Solve. Write the number sentence.**

7. Latasha's plant is 3 inches taller than Maria's plant. Maria's plant is 8 inches high. How tall is Latasha's plant? ______ inches

8. On Monday Vinh's plant was 9 inches tall. After one week it measured 13 inches. How much did it grow? ______ inches

# DAY 5

**Circle the problems that can be solved by making a fast 10. Add.**

| 1. | 2. | 3. | 4. | 5. | 6. | 7. |
|---|---|---|---|---|---|---|
| 9 | 6 | 5 | 7 | 4 | 8 | 4 |
| + 7 | + 8 | + 7 | + 2 | + 8 | + 9 | + 5 |
| 16 | 14 | 12 | 9 | 12 | 17 | 9 |

**Use the chart.**

8. I am an odd number less than 75 and greater than 50. My ones and tens digits are the same number. I am ______.

| 51 | 52 | 53 | 54 | 55 | 56 | 57 | 58 | 59 | 60 |
|---|---|---|---|---|---|---|---|---|---|
| 61 | 62 | 63 | 64 | 65 | 66 | 67 | 68 | 69 | 70 |
| 71 | 72 | 73 | 74 | 75 | 76 | 77 | 78 | 79 | 80 |
| 81 | | | | | | | | | |

# DAY 6

**Add.**

| 1. | 2. | 3. | 4. | 5. |
|---|---|---|---|---|
| 78 | 91 | 105 | 120 | 85 |
| + 13 | + 14 | + 15 | + 16 | + 60 |
| 91 | 105 | 120 | 136 | 145 |

6. Which problem was easiest for you to add and why?

85 plus 60

**Color the odd numbers on the 50 chart.**
**Tell about what you notice.**

7. ______

| 1 | 2 | 3 | 4 | 5 | 6 | 7 | 8 | 9 | 10 |
|---|---|---|---|---|---|---|---|---|---|
| 11 | 12 | 13 | 14 | 15 | 16 | 17 | 18 | 19 | 20 |
| 21 | 22 | 23 | 24 | 25 | 26 | 27 | 28 | 29 | 30 |
| 31 | 32 | 33 | 34 | 35 | 36 | 37 | 38 | 39 | 40 |
| 41 | 42 | 43 | 44 | 45 | 46 | 47 | 48 | 49 | 50 |

# DAY 7

**Add.**

**1.** $136 + 17$ **2.** $153 + 18$ **3.** $171 + 19$ **4.** $190 + 20$ **5.** $127 + 62$

**Compare lengths.**

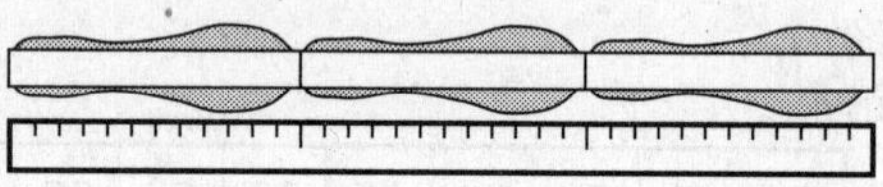

Note: ft = foot; in. = inches; yd = yard

**Write > (greater than), < (less than), or = (equals).**

**6.** 15 in. ___ 1 ft **7.** 2 ft ___ 24 in.

**8.** 1 yd ___ 2 ft **9.** 3 ft ___ 1 yd

# DAY 8

**Circle the problems that need a 10 unbundled. Subtract.**

**1.** 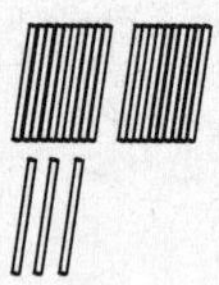 $23 - 8$ **2.** 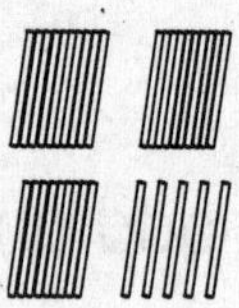 $35 - 4$ **3.** 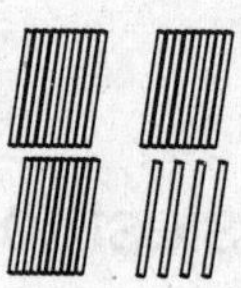 $34 - 9$ **4.** 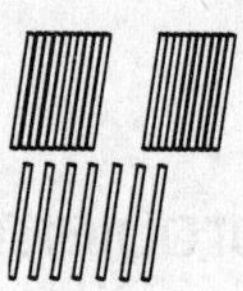 $27 - 8$ **5.** 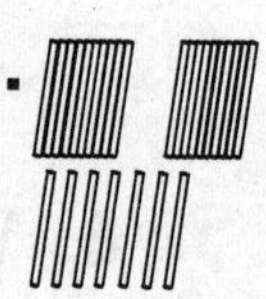 $27 - 8$

**Trade 1 dime for 10 pennies and write the result.**

**6.** 2 dimes 3 pennies = 1 dime ______ pennies

**7.** 4 dimes 6 pennies = 3 dimes ______ pennies

**8.** 3 dimes 1 penny = 2 dimes ______ pennies

**9.** 5 dimes 7 pennies = 4 dimes ______ pennies

# DAY 9

**Subtract. Take a number from 10.**

1. 13 − 9 = 4

> "I can take nine from 10 first. Then I can add the 1 to the number in the ones place."

2. 13 − 5 = ______

> "I can take 5 from 10 first. Then I can add the 5 to the number in the ones place."

3. 13 − 6 = ______
4. 13 − 8 = ______
5. 13 − 10 = ______

**Solve. Write a number sentence.**

6. Jan has a box of 16 crayons and Ryan has a box of 24. How many more crayons are in Ryan's box? ______ crayons ______________

7. Ryan lost 5 of his crayons. How many are in his box now?

   ______ crayons ______________

# DAY 10 CHECKPOINT

**Add.**

| 1. | 2. | 3. | 4. | 5. |
|---|---|---|---|---|
| 56 | 168 | 48 | 13 | 35 |
| + 39 | + 25 | + 23 | + 89 | + 46 |

**Circle the things you would measure with a ruler.**

6.

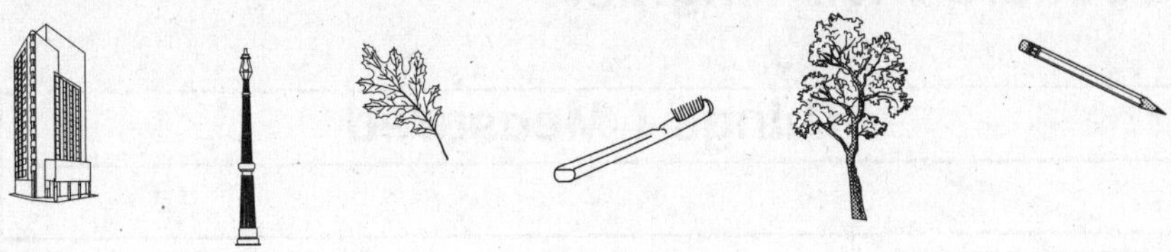

**Add the coins.**

7.

______¢

# DAY 11

Circle the problems that need a 10 unbundled. Subtract.

1. 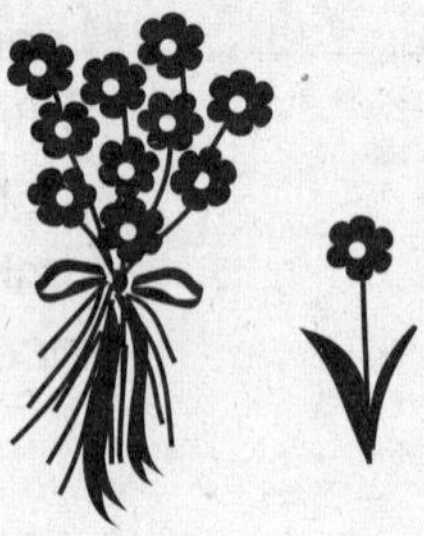

$$\begin{array}{r} 11 \\ -\ 8 \\ \hline \end{array}$$

2. 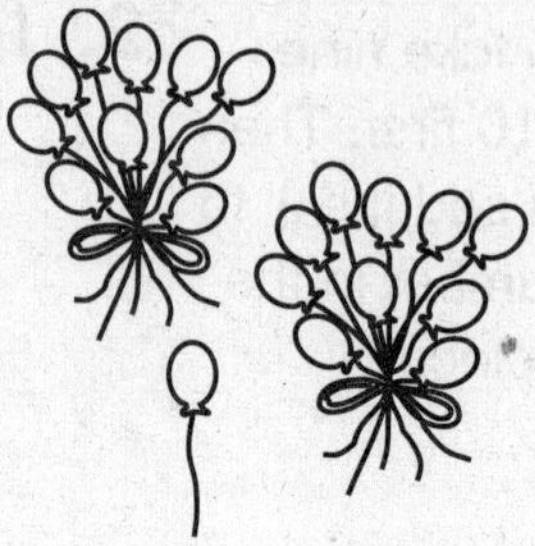

$$\begin{array}{r} 21 \\ -\ 8 \\ \hline \end{array}$$

3. 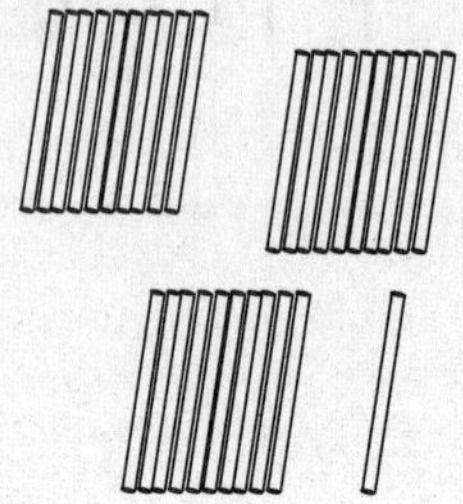

$$\begin{array}{r} 31 \\ -\ 8 \\ \hline \end{array}$$

Continue the pattern.

4. 

A B A C A B A C ____ ____ ____ ____

____ ____ ____ ____

# DAY 12

Subtract. Take a number from 10.

1. $\begin{array}{r} 12 \\ -\ 8 \\ \hline \end{array}$  2. $\begin{array}{r} 12 \\ -\ 5 \\ \hline \end{array}$  3. $\begin{array}{r} 12 \\ -\ 9 \\ \hline \end{array}$  4. $\begin{array}{r} 12 \\ -\ 7 \\ \hline \end{array}$  5. $\begin{array}{r} 12 \\ -\ 4 \\ \hline \end{array}$  6. $\begin{array}{r} 12 \\ -\ 3 \\ \hline \end{array}$

Find the items in your classroom. Measure them to the nearest inch and record their lengths.

7.

| Things I Measured | |
|---|---|
| 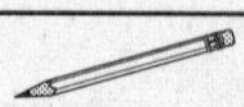 | |
| 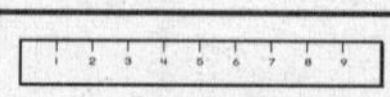 | |
|  | |
| | |
| | |

# DAY 13

**Subtract.**

1. $\begin{array}{r} 14 \\ -\ 9 \\ \hline \end{array}$ 2. $\begin{array}{r} 13 \\ -\ 9 \\ \hline \end{array}$ 3. $\begin{array}{r} 15 \\ -\ 9 \\ \hline \end{array}$ 4. $\begin{array}{r} 17 \\ -\ 9 \\ \hline \end{array}$ 5. $\begin{array}{r} 12 \\ -\ 9 \\ \hline \end{array}$ 6. $\begin{array}{r} 18 \\ -\ 9 \\ \hline \end{array}$ 7. $\begin{array}{r} 16 \\ -\ 9 \\ \hline \end{array}$

**Look at the kitchen items. Draw an X for each shape you see.**

8.

| Kitchen containers | | | | | | |
|---|---|---|---|---|---|---|
| cylinders | | | | | | |
| rectangular boxes | | | | | | |
| cubes | | | | | | |
| cones | | | | | | |
| other | | | | | | |

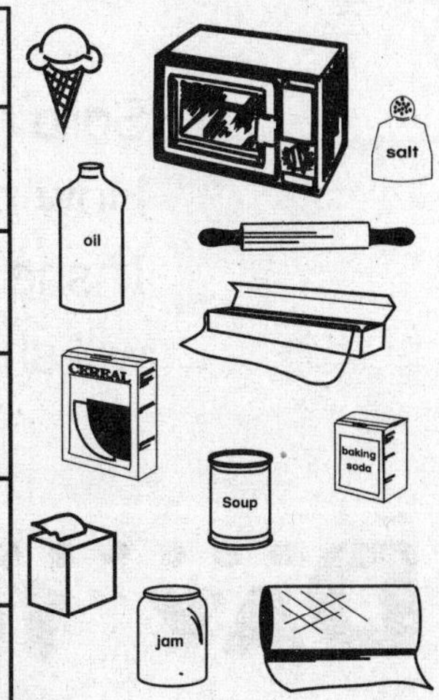


# DAY 14

**Subtract.**

1. $\begin{array}{r} 22 \\ -\ 8 \\ \hline \end{array}$ 2. $\begin{array}{r} 52 \\ -\ 8 \\ \hline \end{array}$ 3. $\begin{array}{r} 92 \\ -\ 8 \\ \hline \end{array}$ 4. $\begin{array}{r} 72 \\ -\ 8 \\ \hline \end{array}$ 5. $\begin{array}{r} 42 \\ -\ 8 \\ \hline \end{array}$ 6. $\begin{array}{r} 82 \\ -\ 8 \\ \hline \end{array}$

**Solve.**

7. Luke has \$1.00. Terri has 3 quarters, 2 dimes, 3 nickels, and 4 pennies. Who has more money? ______________

8. Matt has \$1.00. He buys a bag of chips for \$0.78. His change will be ________.

# DAY 15

**Subtract.**

| **1.** | **2.** | **3.** | **4.** | **5.** | **6.** |
|---|---|---|---|---|---|
| 95 − 7 | 45 − 7 | 65 − 7 | 85 − 7 | 25 − 7 | 55 − 7 |

**Solve.**

**7.** Sara has these coins in her piggy bank.
How much does Sara have? ______¢
If she buys crayons, how much money will she have left? ______¢

# DAY 16

**Circle the problems that need a 10 unbundled. Subtract.**

| **1.** | **2.** | **3.** | **4.** | **5.** | **6.** |
|---|---|---|---|---|---|
| 57 − 3 | 62 − 8 | 91 − 7 | 86 − 4 | 24 − 5 | 44 − 3 |

**Continue the pattern. Add the long minute hand to each clock.**

**7.**

4:00 ______ 4:30 ______ 5:00

**8.** Circle the clock that shows a quarter past 4.

**9.** Draw an X on the time that says quarter 'til 5.

# Day 17

**Count up to find the difference.**

1. $32 - 26$

   "When I count up from 26 to 32, the difference is ______. I count 27, 28, 29, 30, 31, 32."

2. $42 - 16$

   "I can count up ______ to 20, plus 22 more to 42. The difference is ______."

3. $62 - 46$

   "I can count up ______ to 50, plus 12 more to 62. The difference is ______."

4. $52 - 26$

   "I can count up ______ to 30, plus 22 more to 52. The difference is ______."

**Circle the items that hold about 1 liter.**

5. 

# Day 18

**Count up to find the difference.**

1. $36 - 24$
2. $52 - 34$
3. $67 - 34$
4. $92 - 64$
5. $43 - 24$
6. $32 - 16$

**Write > or <.**

7. 361 ◯ 342
8. 205 ◯ 250
9. 278 ◯ 225

10. Put all 6 numbers above in order from least to greatest.

$205 < 225 < \_\_\_\_\_\_ < 278 < \_\_\_\_\_\_ < 361$

(least) (greatest)

# DAY 19

**Count up to find the difference. Then check by unbundling.**

1. $\begin{array}{r} 43 \\ -\ 29 \\ \hline \end{array}$

   "I can count up 1 to get 30, plus 13 more to 43. The difference is ______."

2. $\begin{array}{r} 35 \\ -\ 18 \\ \hline \end{array}$

3. $\begin{array}{r} 45 \\ -\ 18 \\ \hline \end{array}$

4. $\begin{array}{r} 32 \\ -\ 16 \\ \hline \end{array}$

**Solve.**

5. Lisa has 2 quarters, 4 dimes, and 3 nickels.
   Does Lisa have more than $1? Yes No

6. How much more is the total value of her quarters than her dimes? ______¢ than her nickels? ______¢

# DAY 20

**Count up to find the difference. Then circle problems that can be checked by unbundling.**

1. $\begin{array}{r} 41 \\ -\ 27 \\ \hline \end{array}$

2. $\begin{array}{r} 65 \\ -\ 47 \\ \hline \end{array}$

3. $\begin{array}{r} 52 \\ -\ 31 \\ \hline \end{array}$

4. $\begin{array}{r} 36 \\ -\ 18 \\ \hline \end{array}$

5. $\begin{array}{r} 76 \\ -\ 64 \\ \hline \end{array}$

**List 4 ways you can make 44¢ using only dimes and pennies.**

6. ______________________________

7. ______________________________

8. ______________________________

9. ______________________________

# MONTHLY ASSESSMENT

**Use the Calendar.**

**1.** Write the name of the month.

________________ How many days

does this month have? ________

**2.** What month came before this month?

________________

What month comes after this month?

________________

**3.** Describe the pattern of objects.

________________________________________

**4.** Describe the pattern of shapes.

________________________________________

**5.** Describe this pattern with letters. ____________________

**6.** How are the basketball and the soccer ball alike?

________________________________________

**7.** What calendar pieces have cones on them? ________________

What pattern do you notice?

________________________________________

# MONTHLY ASSESSMENT

**Subtract.**

| | | | |
|---|---|---|---|
| **1.** 56 − 24 | **2.** 75 − 34 | **3.** 23 − 10 | **4.** 64 − 32 |
| **5.** 97 − 65 | **6.** 42 − 21 | **7.** 76 − 14 | **8.** 88 − 47 |

**Subtract. Unbundle.**

| | | | |
|---|---|---|---|
| **9.** 43 − 25 | **10.** 87 − 68 | **11.** 32 − 15 | **12.** 84 − 56 |
| **13.** 93 − 28 | **14.** 76 − 28 | **15.** 57 − 29 | **16.** 48 − 29 |

**Add.**

| | | | |
|---|---|---|---|
| **17.** 17 + 34 | **18.** 48 + 16 | **19.** 35 + 23 | **20.** 32 + 19 |
| **21.** 95 + 25 | **22.** 35 + 36 | **23.** 27 + 12 | **24.** 18 + 21 |

**Regroup 1 ten as 10 ones. Write how many.**

| | Start with | End with |
|---|---|---|
| **25.** | 28 = _____ tens _____ ones | 28 = _____ tens _____ ones |
| **26.** | 87 = _____ tens _____ ones | 87 = _____ tens _____ ones |

# MONTHLY ASSESSMENT

**Use the graph to answer the questions.**

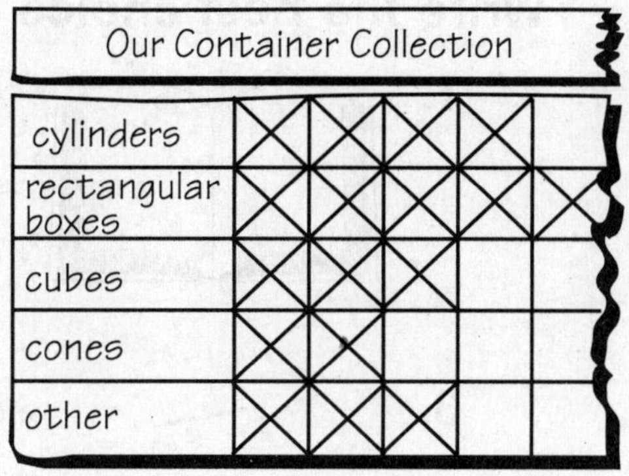


1. What is the graph about?

_______________________________

2. How many different container shapes are there?

_______________________________

3. How many rectangular boxes are there? _______

4. How many more cylinders than cones are there? _______

5. How many containers are there altogether? _______

**Solve.**

6. Jane is making a hat for Emily.
She bought 1 yard of ribbon.
She needs one piece that is 9 inches long.
She needs a second piece that is 18 inches long.
How much ribbon does she need for the hat? _________
Will she have to buy more ribbon? Why or why not?

_____________________________________________________

7. Luis has 2 quarters and 3 dimes. Does he have enough money to buy a book for 75¢? _______

8. Sarah has 1 quarter and 4 dimes. She wants to buy a 69¢ doll. How much more money does she need? _______¢

# MONTHLY ASSESSMENT

**Choose between a ruler and a yardstick.**
**Write the best choice to measure.**

1. 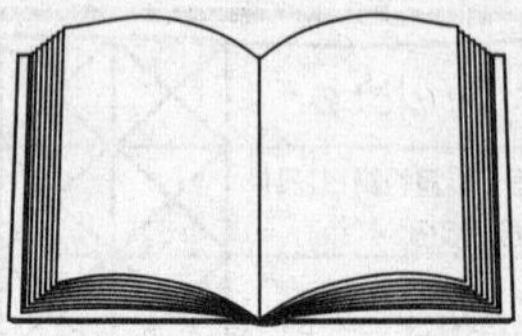 ______________

2. 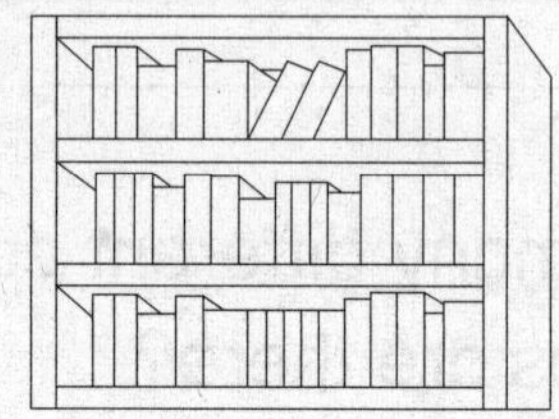 ______________

3. 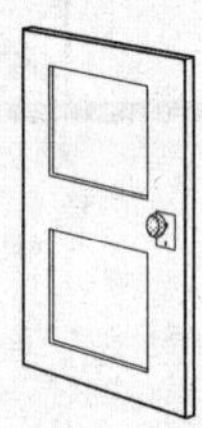 ______________

4. 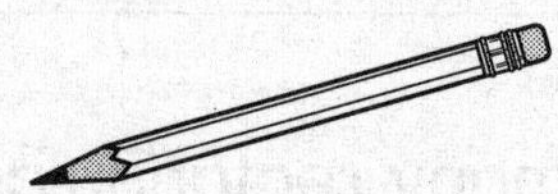 ______________

**Use a ruler to measure.**

5. My scissors are about _______ inches. 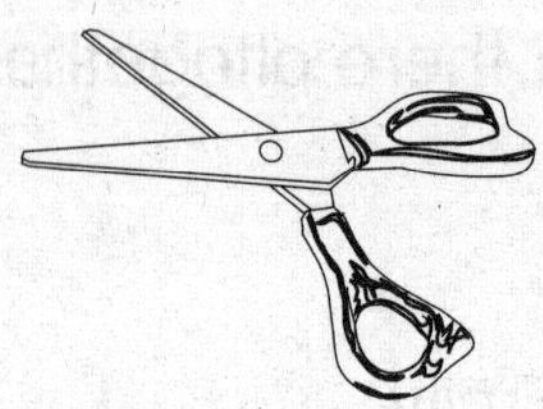

6. My pencil is about _______ inches. 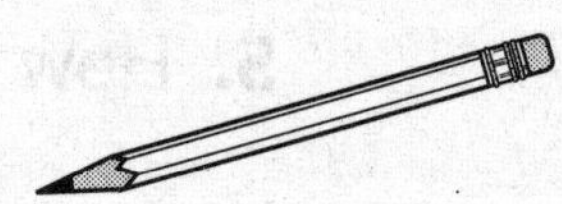

7. My crayon is about _______ inches. 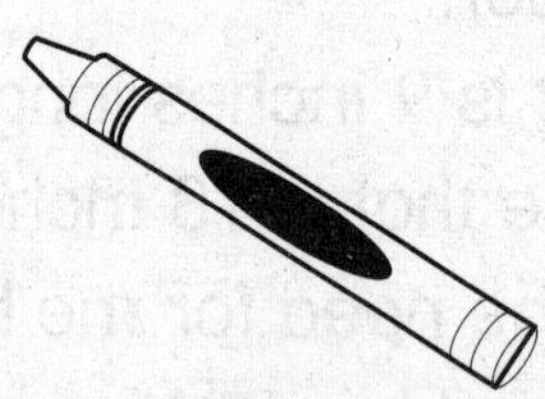

8. My hand is about _______ inches. 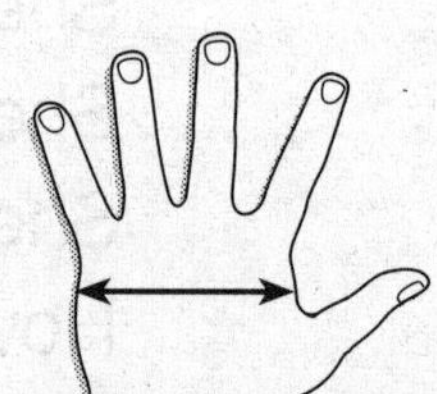

**Count up to find the change for a dollar. Draw an X on the coins.**

9. 

10. 

# DAY 1 APRIL

**Add.**

1.

| Number | 13 | 9 | 11 | 7 |
|---|---|---|---|---|
| +5 | | | | |

2.

| Number | 7 | 6 | 5 | 4 | 3 |
|---|---|---|---|---|---|
| +7 | | | | | |

**Continue the pattern.**

3. 52, 56, 60, ___, ___, ___, ___, ___, ___, ___, ___

4. Are the numbers odd or even? _____

# DAY 2

**Make fact families.**

1. 9 + 8 = ___

___ + ___ = ___

___ − ___ = ___

___ − ___ = ___

2. 9 + 6 = ___

___ + ___ = ___

___ − ___ = ___

___ − ___ = ___

3. 9 + 7 = ___

___ + ___ = ___

___ − ___ = ___

___ − ___ = ___

**Draw hands to show each time.**

4. 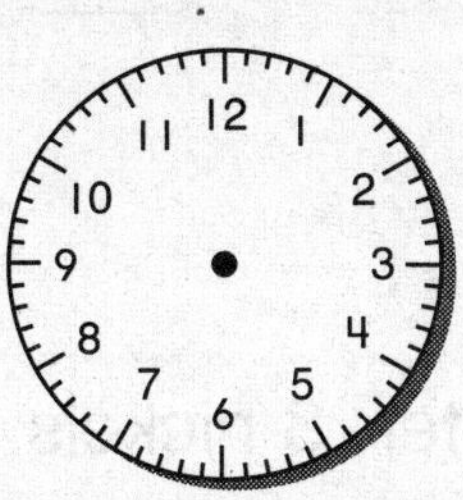


8 : 3 0

5. 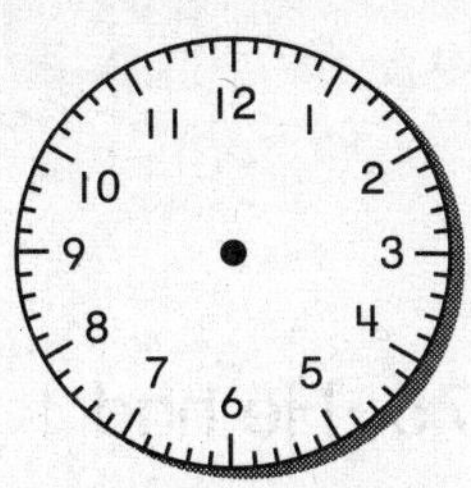


7 : 0 0

6. 

5 : 1 5

7. 

4 : 4 5

# DAY 3

**Add.**

1. 2 + 2
2. 3 + 3
3. 4 + 4
4. 5 + 5
5. 6 + 6
6. 7 + 7
7. 8 + 8
8. 9 + 9
9. 12 + 4
10. 13 + 5
11. 14 + 3
12. 5 + 9
13. 6 + 8
14. 7 + 9
15. 8 + 5
16. 3 + 13

**Color the fraction. Draw an X on the largest fraction.**

17. $\frac{1}{3}$

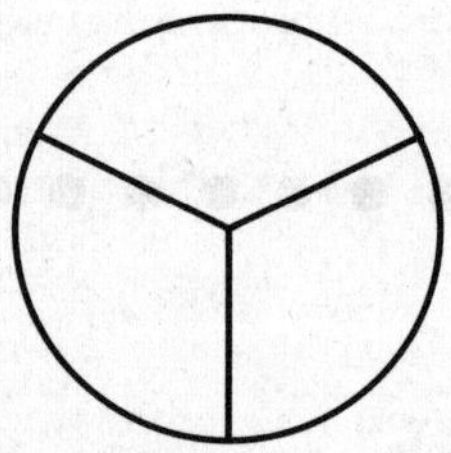

18. $\frac{1}{4}$

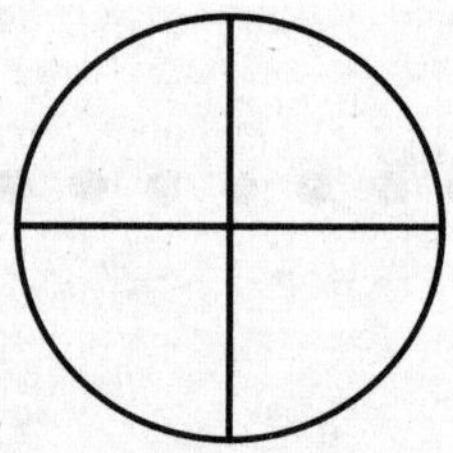

19. $\frac{1}{2}$

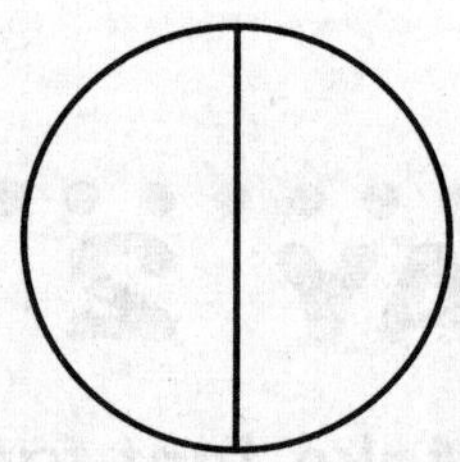

# DAY 4

**Add and subtract. Circle the related facts.**

1. 7 + 8
2. 15 − 7
3. 8 + 7
4. 15 − 8
5. 16 − 9
6. 9 + 7
7. 7 + 9
8. 16 − 7
9. 17 − 7
10. 17 − 10
11. 10 + 7
12. 7 + 10
13. 13 − 6
14. 6 + 7
15. 7 + 6
16. 13 − 7

**Solve.**

17. Darek bought a card for $0.75. He had 1 quarter, 3 nickels, and 4 dimes. Did he have enough money? _______ Did he get change? _______ Explain. ______________________________

# DAY 5

**Add or subtract.**

1.

| Number | 9 | 8 | 7 | 6 | 5 | 4 | 3 |
|---|---|---|---|---|---|---|---|
| +9 | 18 | 17 | | | | | |

2.

| Number | 18 | 17 | 16 | 15 | 14 | 13 | 12 |
|---|---|---|---|---|---|---|---|
| −9 | 9 | 8 | | | | | |

3. What pattern do you see? ______________________________

______________________________________________

**Use clocks to find the fractions.**

4. 

There are _____ minutes in $\frac{1}{3}$ hour.

5. 

There are _____ minutes in $\frac{1}{2}$ hour.

6. 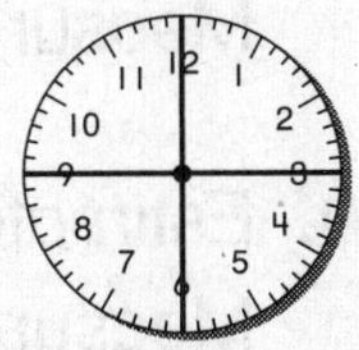

There are _____ minutes in $\frac{1}{4}$ hour.

# DAY 6

**Add.**

1. $\begin{array}{r} 16 \\ +26 \\ \hline \end{array}$ 2. $\begin{array}{r} 37 \\ +42 \\ \hline \end{array}$ 3. $\begin{array}{r} 58 \\ +28 \\ \hline \end{array}$ 4. $\begin{array}{r} 75 \\ +15 \\ \hline \end{array}$ 5. $\begin{array}{r} 29 \\ +30 \\ \hline \end{array}$ 6. $\begin{array}{r} 30 \\ +59 \\ \hline \end{array}$ 7. $\begin{array}{r} 45 \\ +45 \\ \hline \end{array}$ 8. $\begin{array}{r} 15 \\ +28 \\ \hline \end{array}$

**Complete the pattern.**

9. 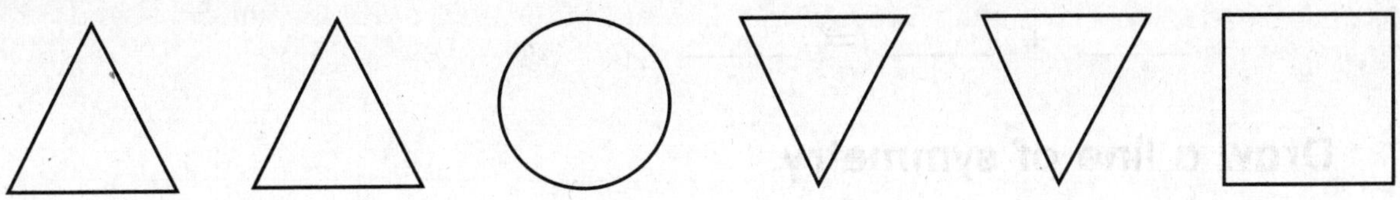

_______ _______ _______ _______ _______ _______

# Day 7

**Add.**

**Circle the problems you regrouped.**

| 1. | 2. | 3. | 4. | 5. | 6. | 7. | 8. |
|---|---|---|---|---|---|---|---|
| 17 | 83 | 28 | 47 | 19 | 26 | 73 | 69 |
| +47 | +19 | +34 | +24 | +67 | +38 | +15 | +15 |

**Estimate and measure. Use a centimeter ruler.**

9. Estimate: ______ centimeters
   Measure: about ______ centimeters

10. Estimate: ______ centimeters
    Measure: about ______ centimeters

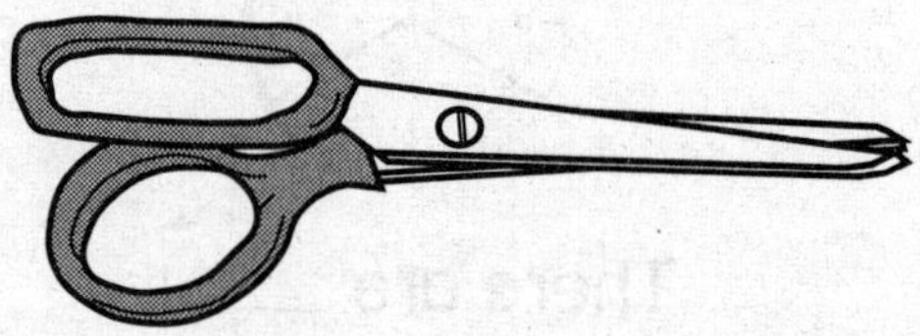

# Day 8

**Use the class Calendar.**

1. Add the dates of the 2nd and the 4th Tuesdays.

   _____ + _____ = _____

2. Add the dates of the 1st and the 3rd Fridays.

   _____ + _____ = _____

3. Add the dates of the 2nd and the 3rd Sundays.

   _____ + _____ = _____

**Draw a line of symmetry.**

4. 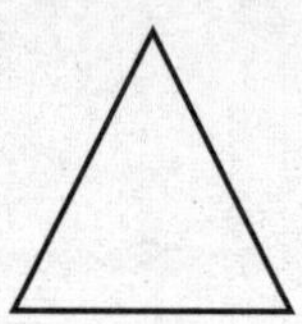

5. 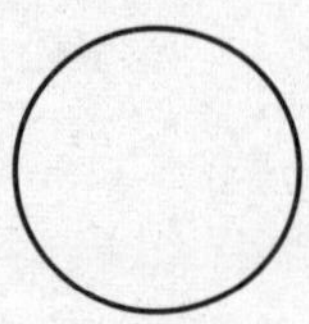

6. 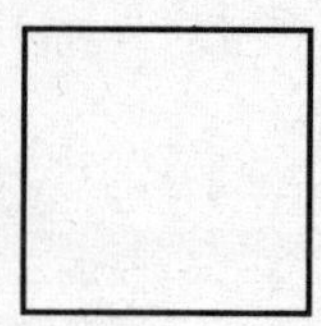

# DAY 9

**Add.**

| 1. | 2. | 3. | 4. | 5. | 6. | 7. | 8. |
|---|---|---|---|---|---|---|---|
| 54 | 86 | 74 | 38 | 35 | 64 | 91 | 85 |
| +28 | +27 | +19 | +43 | +64 | +81 | +28 | +48 |

**Draw to solve.**

Joan ate $\frac{1}{4}$ of the pizza.

Darcy ate $\frac{1}{2}$ of the pizza.

9. Who ate the most pizza?

______________________

10. How much of the pizza was eaten?

______________________

# DAY 10 CHECKPOINT

**Add.**

| 1. | 2. | 3. | 4. | 5. | 6. | 7. |
|---|---|---|---|---|---|---|
| 47 | 23 | 16 | 49 | 63 | 45 | 51 |
| + 28 | + 18 | + 56 | + 38 | + 25 | + 34 | + 19 |

**Color the fraction.**

8. $\frac{1}{2}$

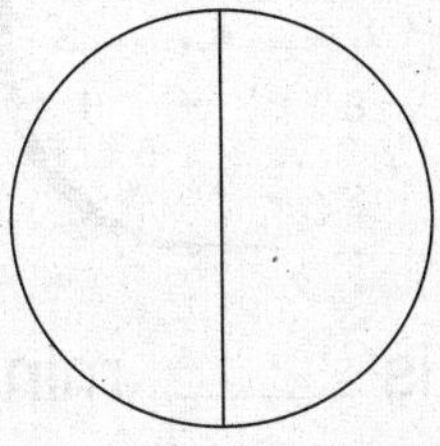

9. $\frac{1}{4}$

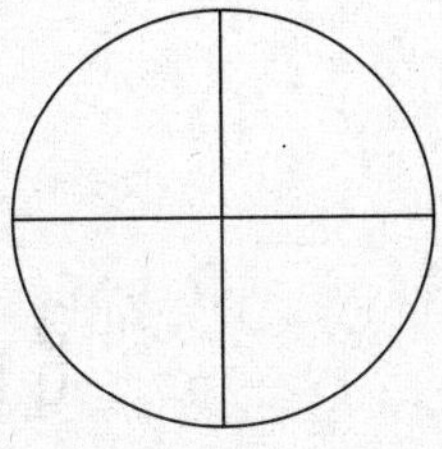

10. $\frac{3}{4}$

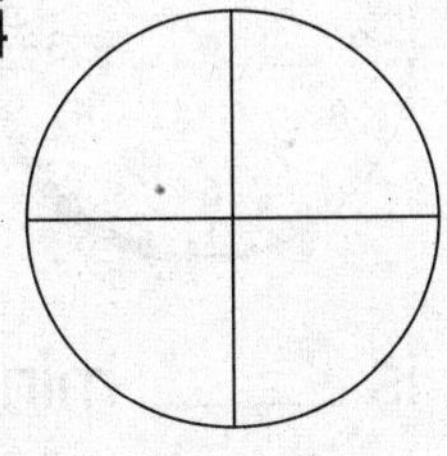

11. $\frac{2}{3}$

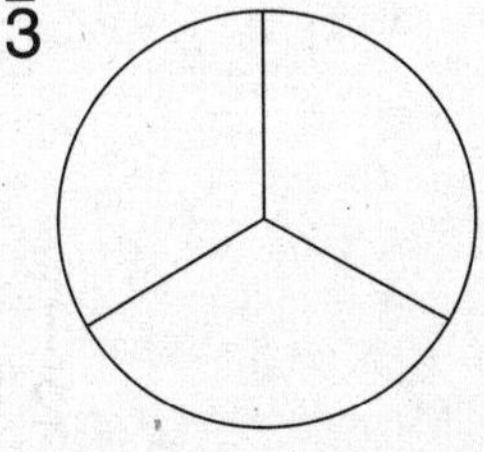

# DAY 11

**Subtract.**

1. $18 - 9$
2. $17 - 6$
3. $16 - 12$
4. $15 - 3$
5. $14 - 7$
6. $13 - 9$
7. $12 - 8$
8. $17 - 9$

**Continue the patterns.**

9. **    ****    ******    ________    ________

10. ***    *****    *******    ________    ________

# DAY 12

**Subtract.**

1.

| Number | 18 | 12 | 8 | 15 | 10 |
|---|---|---|---|---|---|
| −3 | | | | | |

2.

| Number | 17 | 13 | 9 | 11 | 14 |
|---|---|---|---|---|---|
| −4 | | | | | |

**Draw hands to show the fraction.**

3.

$\frac{1}{4}$ hour is ______ minutes.

4.

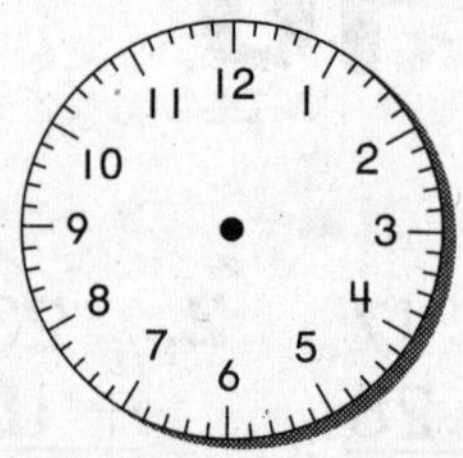

$\frac{1}{3}$ hour is ______ minutes.

5.

$\frac{1}{2}$ hour is ______ minutes.

6.

$\frac{3}{4}$ hour is ______ minutes.

# DAY 13

**Subtract.**

1. $\begin{array}{r} 47 \\ -28 \\ \hline \end{array}$ 2. $\begin{array}{r} 54 \\ -27 \\ \hline \end{array}$ 3. $\begin{array}{r} 38 \\ -19 \\ \hline \end{array}$ 4. $\begin{array}{r} 23 \\ -7 \\ \hline \end{array}$ 5. $\begin{array}{r} 72 \\ -54 \\ \hline \end{array}$ 6. $\begin{array}{r} 68 \\ -39 \\ \hline \end{array}$ 7. $\begin{array}{r} 82 \\ -37 \\ \hline \end{array}$

**Trace the lines. Write the number of lines and parts.**

8. 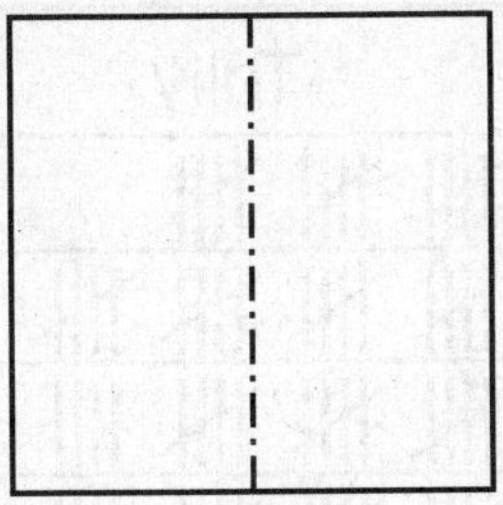

_____ lines

_____ parts

9. 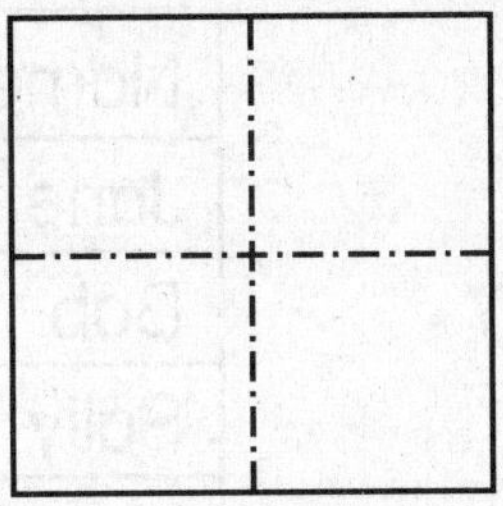

_____ lines

_____ parts

10. 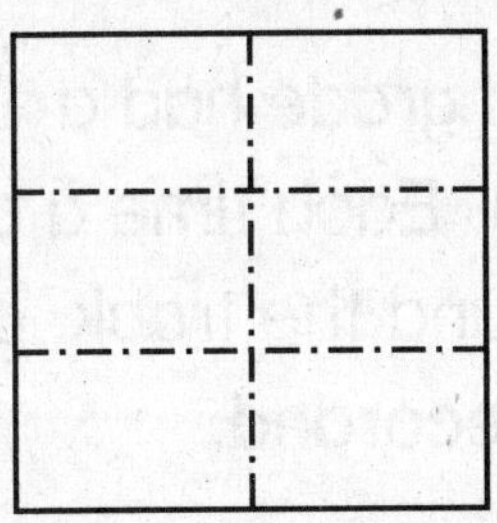

_____ lines

_____ parts

11. 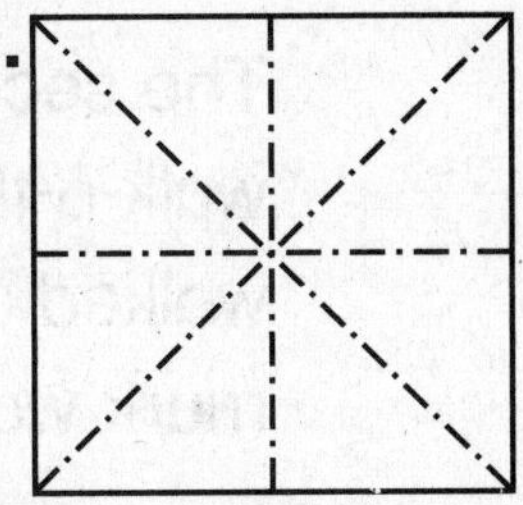

_____ lines

_____ parts

12. What pattern do you see? ______________________________

______________________________

# DAY 14

**Subtract. Circle when you unbundle a ten.**

1. $\begin{array}{r} 37 \\ -18 \\ \hline \end{array}$ 2. $\begin{array}{r} 54 \\ -36 \\ \hline \end{array}$ 3. $\begin{array}{r} 39 \\ -25 \\ \hline \end{array}$ 4. $\begin{array}{r} 95 \\ -17 \\ \hline \end{array}$ 5. $\begin{array}{r} 75 \\ -24 \\ \hline \end{array}$ 6. $\begin{array}{r} 43 \\ -16 \\ \hline \end{array}$ 7. $\begin{array}{r} 28 \\ -19 \\ \hline \end{array}$

**Write the time.**

8. Dan looked at his watch. It was 4:30.
"The circus will start in 2 hours," he told Jim.
What time will the circus start? _____

# Day 15

**Subtract.**

1. $67 - 29$ 2. $35 - 17$ 3. $28 - 19$ 4. $62 - 37$ 5. $78 - 39$ 6. $48 - 29$ 7. $27 - 9$

**Use the chart. Answer the questions.**

The second grade had a walk-a-thon. Each time a child walked around the track, a tally mark was recorded.

| Name | Tally | Total |
|---|---|---|
| Jane | 𝍸 𝍸 𝍸 | 15 |
| Bob | 𝍸 𝍸 𝍸 𝍸 ||| | 23 |
| Sally | 𝍸 𝍸 𝍸 |||| | 19 |
| Kim | 𝍸 𝍸 𝍸 𝍸 𝍸 | 25 |

8. Who walked the most? ______

9. Who walked the least? ______

10. How many more tally marks does Bob have than Sally? ______

# Day 16

**Subtract.**

1. $43 - 19$ 2. $67 - 20$ 3. $38 - 19$ 4. $25 - 8$ 5. $47 - 16$ 6. $31 - 19$ 7. $45 - 27$

**Continue the patterns.**

8. 21, 24, 27, ______, ______, ______, ______

9. 40, 44, 48, ______, ______, ______, ______, ______

# DAY 17

**Make 2 subtraction problems with the numbers.**

1. 20, 45, 25

___ − ___ = ___

___ − ___ = ___

2. 18, 37, 19

___ − ___ = ___

___ − ___ = ___

3. 29, 16, 13

___ − ___ = ___

___ − ___ = ___

**Guess my coins.**

4. I have $0.75.
I have nickels, dimes, and quarters.
I have 8 coins.
What coins do I have? ______________________

# DAY 18

**Subtract.**

| 1. | 2. | 3. | 4. | 5. | 6. | 7. |
|---|---|---|---|---|---|---|
| 47 | 61 | 23 | 49 | 58 | 32 | 89 |
| −16 | −14 | −14 | −27 | −19 | −17 | −37 |

**Find the 0. Circle tens or ones.**

8. 650 tens ones

9. 605 tens ones

10. 560 tens ones

11. 506 tens ones

12. 490 tens ones

**Make the largest number.**

13. 5, 8, 3 ______

14. 4, 9, 7 ______

15. 7, 1, 3 ______

# DAY 19

**Subtract.**

Look at the class Calendar. Make 6 subtraction problems using dates.

1. ☐ − ☐ ____  2. ☐ − ☐ ____  3. ☐ − ☐ ____  4. ☐ − ☐ ____  5. ☐ − ☐ ____  6. ☐ − ☐ ____

**Solve.**

7. Two second grade classes are going to the aquarium.
Mrs. Torres has 25 students in her class.
Mrs. Chan has 27 students in her class.
5 adults are also going. The bus can hold 64 people.
Is there enough room on the bus? ______
How many people are going? ______ people

# DAY 20

**Subtract.**

| 1. | 2. | 3. | 4. | 5. | 6. | 7. | 8. |
|---|---|---|---|---|---|---|---|
| 89 | 98 | 15 | 76 | 73 | 97 | 38 | 27 |
| −24 | −79 | −10 | −49 | −52 | −68 | −21 | −16 |

**Solve.**

9. 37 people are going on the field trip. The bus company has 2 buses. One bus will hold 46 people. The other will hold 27 people. Which bus should they use? ______
Why? ______
______
How many empty seats will there be? ______ seats

# MONTHLY ASSESSMENT

**Use the Calendar.**

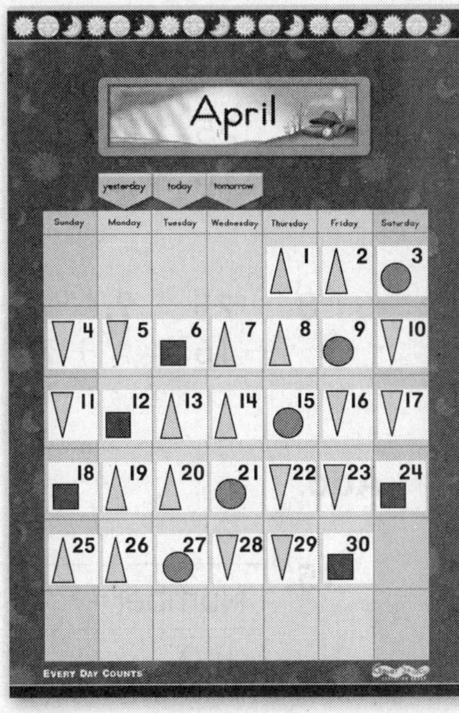


1. Write the name of the month.

   ________________ How many days

   does this month have? ________

2. Name two other months that have 30 days.

   ______________________________

3. Describe the pattern of shapes.

   ______________________________

   ______________________________

4. How are the triangles alike?

   ______________________________

5. How are the triangles different?

   ______________________________

6. List each the number that appears on a circle or square.

   ______________________________

   What do you notice about these numbers?

   ______________________________

   ______________________________

# MONTHLY ASSESSMENT

**Add or subtract.**

1. $\begin{array}{r} 25 \\ +16 \\ \hline \end{array}$ 2. $\begin{array}{r} 42 \\ -31 \\ \hline \end{array}$ 3. $\begin{array}{r} 16 \\ +48 \\ \hline \end{array}$ 4. $\begin{array}{r} 29 \\ +20 \\ \hline \end{array}$ 5. $\begin{array}{r} 87 \\ -23 \\ \hline \end{array}$ 6. $\begin{array}{r} 94 \\ -67 \\ \hline \end{array}$ 7. $\begin{array}{r} 33 \\ +67 \\ \hline \end{array}$

8. $\begin{array}{r} 75 \\ +16 \\ \hline \end{array}$ 9. $\begin{array}{r} 19 \\ +78 \\ \hline \end{array}$ 10. $\begin{array}{r} 38 \\ -14 \\ \hline \end{array}$ 11. $\begin{array}{r} 76 \\ +19 \\ \hline \end{array}$ 12. $\begin{array}{r} 28 \\ -18 \\ \hline \end{array}$ 13. $\begin{array}{r} 49 \\ +51 \\ \hline \end{array}$ 14. $\begin{array}{r} 59 \\ -16 \\ \hline \end{array}$

**Add.**

15.

| Number | 12 | 15 | 14 | 13 | 8 | 5 | 6 | 2 |
|---|---|---|---|---|---|---|---|---|
| + 3 | | | | | | | | |

**Subtract.**

16.

| Number | 12 | 15 | 14 | 13 | 16 | 18 | 17 | 9 |
|---|---|---|---|---|---|---|---|---|
| − 5 | | | | | | | | |

**Add.**

17.

| Number | 7 | 27 | 14 | 4 | 19 | 69 | 3 | 43 |
|---|---|---|---|---|---|---|---|---|
| + 10 | | | | | | | | |

**Find the 0. Circle tens or ones.**

18. 730 tens ones

19. 703 tens ones

20. 260 tens ones

21. 602 tens ones

# MONTHLY ASSESSMENT

**Guess my coins.**

**1.** I have 87 cents.
I have 8 coins.
I have ________________
________________

**2.** I have 73 cents.
I have 9 coins.
I have ________________
________________

**Use the chart.**

The second grade had a math contest. The children made 3 teams. They received a tally mark for every math problem solved correctly.

| Second Grade Math Contest | |
|---|---|
| Team 1 | 卌 卌 卌 卌 卌 卌 卌 卌 卌 卌 \|\|\|\| |
| Team 2 | 卌 卌 卌 卌 卌 卌 卌 卌 卌 卌 卌 卌 \|\|\| |
| Team 3 | 卌 卌 卌 卌 卌 \|\|\| |

**3.** Which team won the contest?
________

Show your work.

**4.** How many more problems did Team 2 solve than Team 3?
______ problems

____ − ____ = ____

**5.** How many problems did Team 1 and Team 3 solve together?
______ problems

____ + ____ = ____

**6.** How many problems were solved by all three teams together? ______ problems

____ + ____ + ____ = ____

# MONTHLY ASSESSMENT

**Draw a line of symmetry.**

**1.** 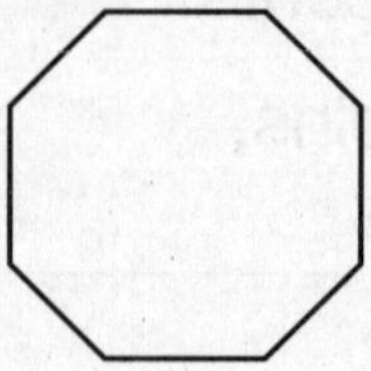

**2.** 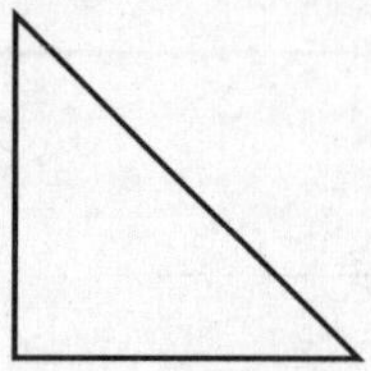

**3.** 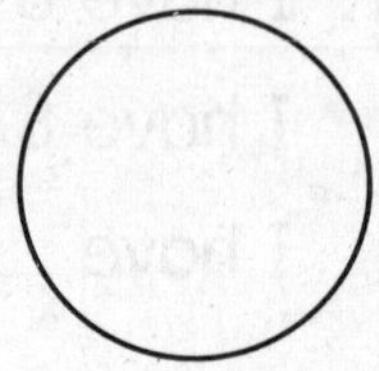

**Do the coins make a dollar? Write yes or no.**

| | quarters | dimes | nickels | pennies | yes or no |
|---|---|---|---|---|---|
| **4.** | 1 | 5 | 3 | 10 | |
| **5.** | 2 | 2 | 1 | 20 | |
| **6.** | 1 | 4 | 3 | 2 | |
| **7.** | | | | 100 | |
| **8.** | 4 | | | | |
| **9.** | | 8 | 2 | | |
| **10.** | | | 10 | 14 | |

**Estimate and measure. Use a centimeter ruler.**

**11.** Estimate: ________ centimeters
Measure: about ________ centimeters

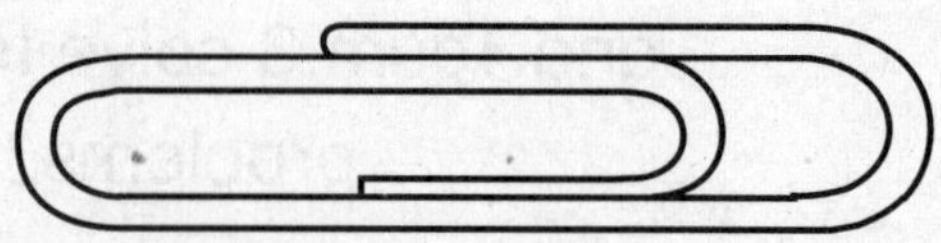

**12.** Estimate: ________ centimeters Measure: about ________ centimeters

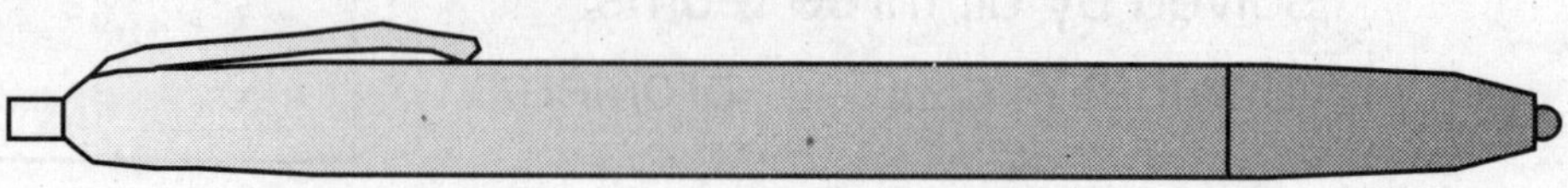

# DAY 1 MAY/JUNE

**Add.**

1. Draw 2 dots in each circle.

___ + ___ + ___ = ___

___ groups of ___ = ___

2. Draw 3 dots in each circle.

___ + ___ + ___ + ___ = ___

___ groups of ___ = ___

**Write the pattern.**

3. ____ ears ____ ears ____ ears ____ ears

# DAY 2

**Add.**

1. Draw 5 dots in each circle.

___ + ___ = ___

___ groups of ___ = ___

2. Draw 2 dots in each circle.

___ + ___ + ___ + ___ + ___ = ___

___ groups of ___ = ___

**Add.**

3. 10 + 8 = ___ 4. 7 + 9 = ___ 5. 6 + 8 = ___ 6. 5 + 7 = ___

**Make change from $1.00.**

7. You spend 65¢.

______¢

8. You spend 34¢.

______¢

# Day 3

**Add or subtract.**

1. $15 + 3$ 2. $18 - 10$ 3. $13 + 7$ 4. $14 - 9$ 5. $17 - 12$ 6. $15 - 13$ 7. $14 + 4$ 8. $15 + 3$

**Draw a shape that is congruent.**

9. 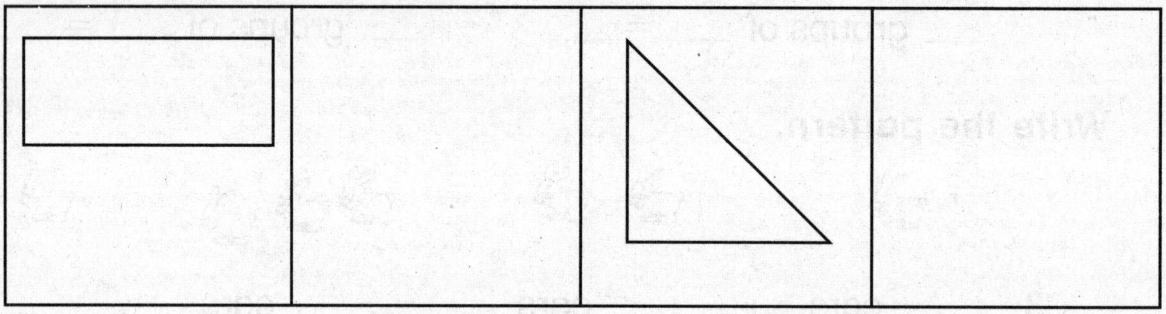

# Day 4

**Add.**

1. Draw 3 circles.
   Put 5 dots in each.

   ___ + ___ + ___ = ___

   ___ groups of ___ = ___

2. Draw 4 dots in each circle.

   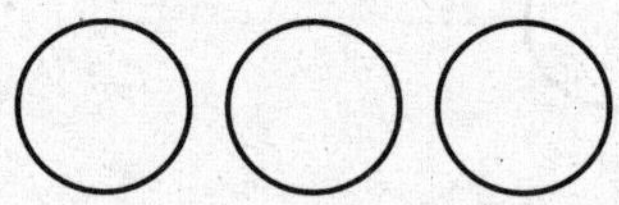

   ___ + ___ + ___ = ___

   ___ groups of ___ = ___

3. 18 − 10 = ___ 4. 16 − 8 = ___ 5. 15 − 7 = ___ 6. 10 − 2 = ___

**Solve.**

7. One Tuesday, the temperature in Miami was 85 degrees outside. On the same day, the temperature in Alaska was 47 degrees. How much warmer was it in Miami than in Alaska? ______ degrees

# DAY 5

**Draw and add.**

1\.

2 groups of 6

___ + ___ = ___

2\.

4 groups of 2

___ + ___ + ___ + ___ = ___

**3.** 47 + 16 = ___ **4.** 28 + 35 = ___ **5.** 39 + 19 = ___ **6.** 27 + 19 = ___

**Estimate how many. Write your estimate.**
**Circle the groups of 10 and count.**

**7.** Estimate: __________ Check: __________

# DAY 6

**Draw the pictures. Write the number sentences.**

1\.

5 groups of 3

__ + __ + __ + __ + __ = __

2\.

6 groups of 3

__ + __ + __ + __ + __ + __ = __

**Continue the pattern.**

**3.** 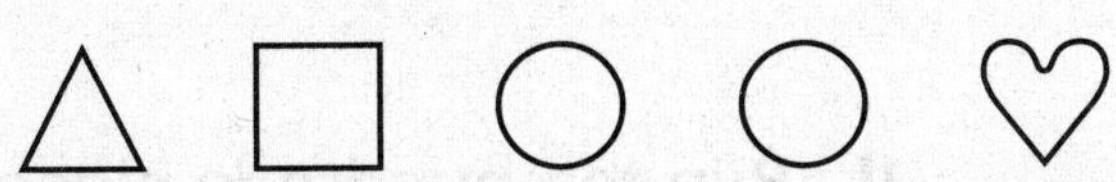

A B C C D ___ ___ ___ ___ ___

___ ___ ___ ___ ___

# DAY 7

**Write the number sentences.**

1.

___ + ___ = ___

___ groups of ___ = ___.

2.

___ + ___ = ___

___ groups of ___ = ___.

**Circle the answer.**

3. Is 1 pint more or less than 1 cup?

more    less

4. Is 1 cup more or less than 1 quart?

more    less

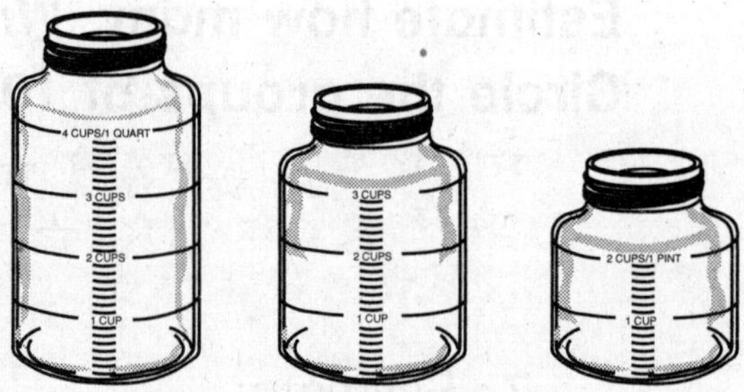


# DAY 8

**Write the number sentences.**

1.

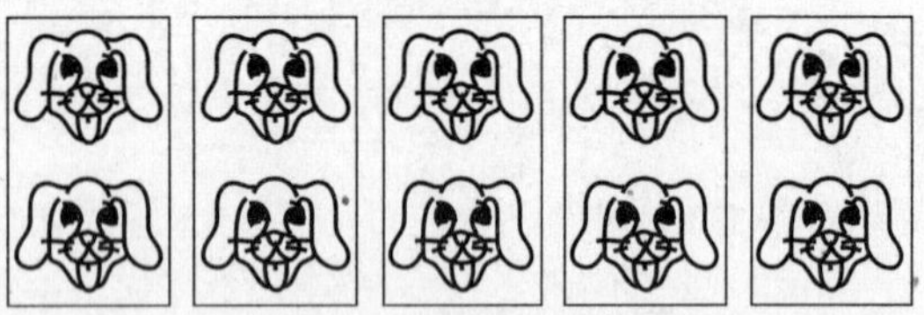

___ + ___ + ___ + ___ + ___ = ___

___ groups of ___ = ___.

2.

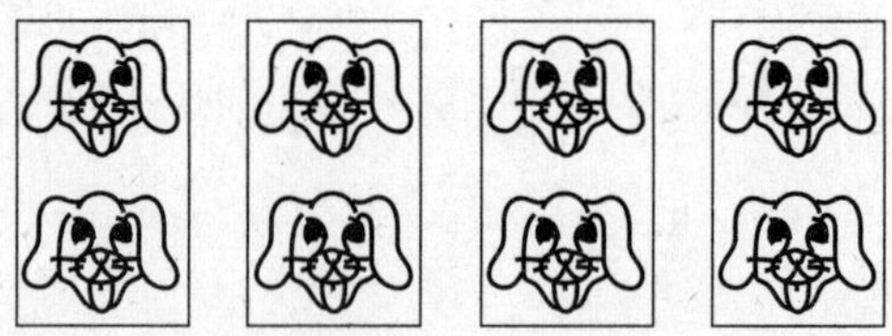

___ + ___ + ___ + ___ = ___

___ groups of ___ = ___.

**Write a 3-digit number.**

3. 5 in the ones place ______

4. 8 in the hundreds place ______

5. 0 in the tens place ______

6. 9 in the tens place ______

# DAY 9

**Draw the pictures. Write the number sentences.**

**1.**

3 groups of 5 = ___.

___ + ___ + ___ = ___

**2.**

5 groups of 1 = ___.

___ + ___ + ___ + ___ + ___ = ___

**Solve.**

**3.** Maria had 4 flower vases.
She put 3 roses in each vase.
How many roses did Maria have? _____ roses
Show your work. ____________________

# DAY 10 CHECKPOINT

**Add or subtract.**

| **1.** | **2.** | **3.** | **4.** | **5.** | **6.** | **7.** | **8.** | **9.** |
|---|---|---|---|---|---|---|---|---|
| $\begin{array}{r} 9 \\ +\ 9 \\ \hline \end{array}$ | $\begin{array}{r} 8 \\ +\ 7 \\ \hline \end{array}$ | $\begin{array}{r} 7 \\ +\ 9 \\ \hline \end{array}$ | $\begin{array}{r} 4 \\ +\ 8 \\ \hline \end{array}$ | $\begin{array}{r} 3 \\ +\ 9 \\ \hline \end{array}$ | $\begin{array}{r} 18 \\ -\ 3 \\ \hline \end{array}$ | $\begin{array}{r} 17 \\ -\ 8 \\ \hline \end{array}$ | $\begin{array}{r} 16 \\ -\ 9 \\ \hline \end{array}$ | $\begin{array}{r} 14 \\ -\ 7 \\ \hline \end{array}$ |

**Write the number sentences.**

**10.**

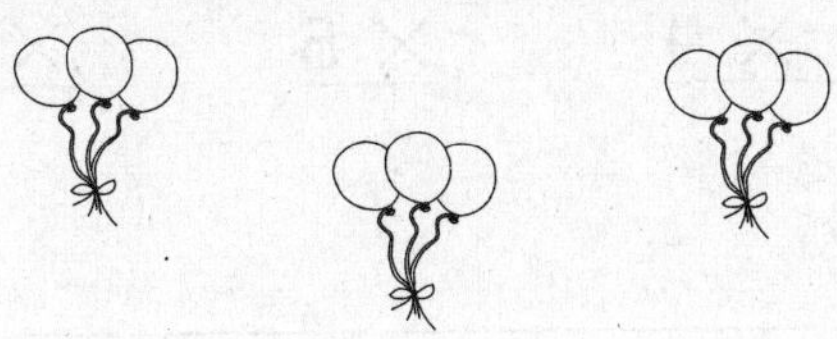

___ + ___ + ___ = ___

___ groups of ___ = ___.

**11.**

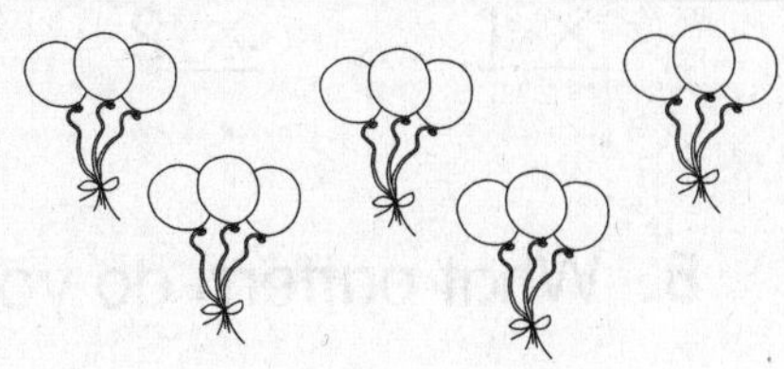

___ + ___ + ___ + ___ + ___ = ___

___ groups of ___ = ___.

**Make the change from $1.00.**

**12.** You spend 45¢. _____¢

**13.** You spent 63¢. _____¢

# DAY 11

**Multiply. You may draw pictures.**

1. $2 \times 3$ 2. $3 \times 2$ 3. $2 \times 1$ 4. $4 \times 3$ 5. $3 \times 4$ 6. $1 \times 4$ 7. $1 \times 5$ 8. $2 \times 2$

9. Circle the ones that were easy for you. Why do you think they were easy? ______________________________

______________________________

**Skip count to continue the patterns.**

10. 10, 12, 14, ______, ______, ______, ______, ______

11. 15, 20, 25, ______, ______, ______, ______, ______

12. How can skip-counting help you in multiplication? ______________

______________________________

# DAY 12

**Multiply.**

1. $3 \times 1$ 2. $3 \times 2$ 3. $3 \times 3$ 4. $3 \times 4$ 5. $3 \times 5$ 6. $3 \times 6$ 7. $3 \times 7$

8. What pattern do you see? ______________________________

**Write yes or no.**

9. Manuel has 1 pint of milk. Can he make pudding that uses 2 cups of milk? ________

10. Marie has 1 quart of milk. She and 2 friends each drink 1 cup of milk. Does she have any milk left? ________

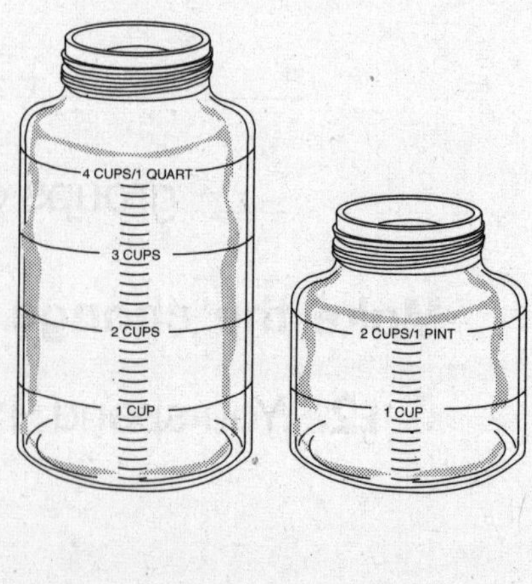

# Day 13

**Multiply. Use skip-counting.**

| **1.** | **2.** | **3.** | **4.** | **5.** | **6.** | **7.** | **8.** | **9.** |
|---|---|---|---|---|---|---|---|---|
| 5 | 5 | 5 | 5 | 5 | 5 | 5 | 5 | 5 |
| × 1 | × 2 | × 3 | × 4 | × 5 | × 6 | × 7 | × 8 | × 9 |

**Circle rolls or stacks.**

**10.**

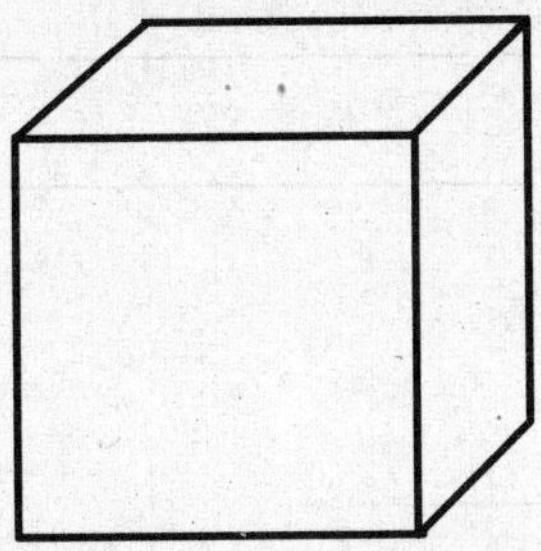

rolls stacks

**11.**

rolls stacks

**12.**

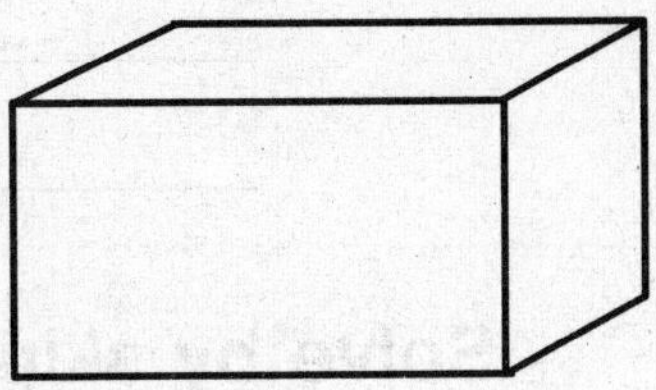

rolls stacks

# Day 14

**Multiply.**

| **1.** | **2.** | **3.** | **4.** | **5.** | **6.** | **7.** | **8.** |
|---|---|---|---|---|---|---|---|
| 2 | 4 | 3 | 5 | 2 | 4 | 3 | 5 |
| × 6 | × 3 | × 5 | × 4 | × 7 | × 2 | × 2 | × 5 |

**Solve. Use repeated addition.**

**9.** Joe walks 5 miles to school every day.
How many miles does he walk in 5 days? ______ miles
Show your work. ____________________

# Day 15

**Add, subtract, or multiply.**

| 1. | 2. | 3. | 4. | 5. | 6. | 7. | 8. | 9. |
|---|---|---|---|---|---|---|---|---|
| 2 | 2 | 4 | 5 | 5 | 10 | 6 | 6 | 12 |
| × 2 | + 2 | − 2 | + 5 | × 2 | − 5 | + 6 | × 2 | − 6 |

**10.** What do you notice about adding doubles and multiplying by 2?

______________________________________________

______________________________________________

**Solve by skip-counting.**

**11.** How many hands do 9 children have? ______

**12.** Write a multiplication fact for this. ____ × ____ = ____

# Day 16

**Add or subtract.**

| 1. | 2. | 3. | 4. | 5. | 6. | 7. |
|---|---|---|---|---|---|---|
| 18 | 17 | 16 | 15 | 14 | 13 | 12 |
| + 0 | − 4 | + 2 | − 9 | + 3 | − 9 | + 6 |

| 8. | 9. | 10. | 11. | 12. | 13. | 14. |
|---|---|---|---|---|---|---|
| 25 | 43 | 38 | 95 | 62 | 49 | 77 |
| + 88 | + 58 | + 74 | + 21 | + 12 | + 15 | + 26 |

**Continue the patterns.**

**15.** 25, 35, 45, ______, ______, ______, ______, ______, ______

**16.** 1, 2, 4, 8, ______, ______, ______, ______

# DAY 17

**Subtract or multiply.**

1. $3 \times 3$
2. $5 \times 3$
3. $7 \times 2$
4. $5 \times 2$
5. $2 \times 5$
6. $6 \times 2$
7. $3 \times 4$
8. $1 \times 6$
9. $9 \times 2$
10. $10 \times 1$
11. $23 - 17$
12. $48 - 29$
13. $78 - 47$
14. $43 - 19$
15. $87 - 29$
16. $42 - 37$

**Choose the best tool. Match.**

17. centimeters feet pints yards

# DAY 18

**Write facts using the numbers. Watch the signs.**

| 1. 10, 8, 2 | 2. 3, 5, 15 | 3. 4, 2, 8 | 4. 2, 6, 12 |
|---|---|---|---|
| __ + __ = __ | __ × __ = __ | __ × __ = __ | __ × __ = __ |
| __ + __ = __ | __ × __ = __ | __ × __ = __ | __ × __ = __ |
| __ − __ = __ | | | |
| __ − __ = __ | | | |

**Who am I?**

5. I am a 3-digit number. I have a 0 in the ones place.
I have a 3 in the hundreds place. If you add my digits, the sum is 5.
Who am I? ______

# DAY 19

**Multiply.**

1. $\begin{array}{r} 5 \\ \times 1 \\ \hline \end{array}$  2. $\begin{array}{r} 5 \\ \times 2 \\ \hline \end{array}$  3. $\begin{array}{r} 5 \\ \times 3 \\ \hline \end{array}$  4. $\begin{array}{r} 5 \\ \times 4 \\ \hline \end{array}$  5. $\begin{array}{r} 5 \\ \times 5 \\ \hline \end{array}$  6. $\begin{array}{r} 5 \\ \times 6 \\ \hline \end{array}$

7. $\begin{array}{r} 4 \\ \times 1 \\ \hline \end{array}$  8. $\begin{array}{r} 4 \\ \times 2 \\ \hline \end{array}$  9. $\begin{array}{r} 4 \\ \times 3 \\ \hline \end{array}$  10. $\begin{array}{r} 4 \\ \times 4 \\ \hline \end{array}$  11. $\begin{array}{r} 4 \\ \times 5 \\ \hline \end{array}$  12. $\begin{array}{r} 4 \\ \times 6 \\ \hline \end{array}$

**Solve.**

13. There are 6 cows in the field. How many legs do 6 cows have?

_______

14. How did you solve this? ________________________________________

________________________________________________________________

# DAY 20

**Write 1 addition, 1 subtraction, and 1 multiplication sentence for each answer below.**

1. ___ + ___ = 10    ___ − ___ = 10    ___ × ___ = 10

2. ___ + ___ = 8    ___ − ___ = 8    ___ × ___ = 8

**Solve.**

3. How many ways can you put 8 into equal groups? _______

Write the number sentence for each way.

____________________    ____________________

# MONTHLY ASSESSMENT

**Use the Calendar.**

**1.** Write the name of the month.

________________ How many days

does this month have? ________

**2.** Name two other months with 31 days.

____________________________________

**3.** What day of the week is the first of the month?

____________________

**4.** What day of the week is the 31st? ____________________

**5.** Fill in this chart:

| **Number of tricycles** | **Number of bicycles** |
|---|---|
| 1 | |
| 1 | |
| 1 | |
| 1 | |
| 1 | |

**6.** What do you notice every time there is a tricycle?

__________________________________________________________

__________________________________________________________

# MONTHLY ASSESSMENT

**Multiply.**

1. $2 \times 2$
2. $4 \times 2$
3. $5 \times 3$
4. $7 \times 3$
5. $9 \times 2$
6. $8 \times 2$
7. $6 \times 2$
8. $1 \times 3$
9. $3 \times 2$
10. $1 \times 5$
11. $4 \times 5$
12. $3 \times 5$
13. $2 \times 5$
14. $6 \times 5$
15. $7 \times 5$
16. $5 \times 5$

**Add or subtract.**

17. $28 + 19$
18. $10 + 57$
19. $38 - 16$
20. $18 - 8$
21. $74 - 23$
22. $93 - 42$
23. $84 - 65$

**Write an addition sentence for each picture.**

24.

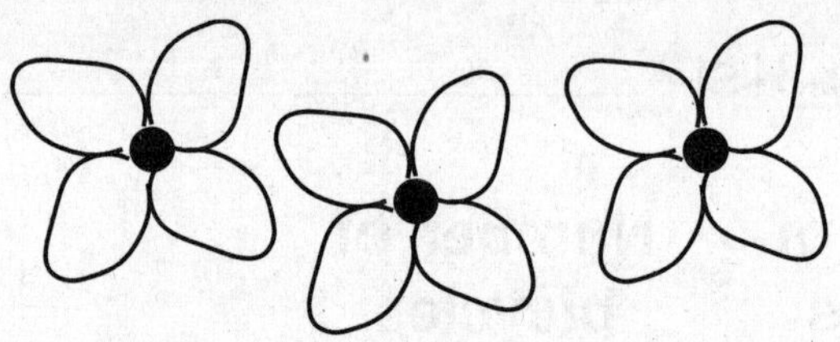

___ + ___ + ___ = ___

___ sets of ___ = ___.

25.

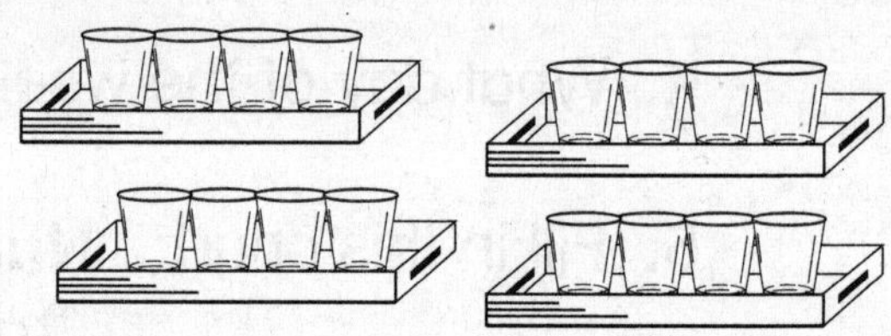

___ + ___ + ___ + ___ = ___

___ sets of ___ = ___.

**Draw the picture. Write how many.**

26.

$4 \times 3 =$ ______

27.

$2 \times 6 =$ ______

# MONTHLY ASSESSMENT

**Solve.**

1. Aaron planted a garden.
He planted 8 rows with 5 plants in each row.
How many plants are there all together?
Write the number sentence and draw the picture. ____________________

2. Juan, Lu, and Anna help Aaron in the garden.
They each work for 2 hours every week.
How many hours do the children work every week? ______ hours

3. Aaron saw 3 rabbits in the garden.
He saw 3 deer and 3 squirrels, too.
How many animals did he see in the garden? ______ animals

**Circle the answer.**

4. Aaron, Juan, and Anna each took 2 pictures of the garden.
Who took more pictures?

girls boys

5. The children had a snack after they worked in the garden.
Each child had 4 crackers.
How many crackers were eaten? ______ crackers

# MONTHLY ASSESSMENT

**Complete the chart.**
**Write yes or no.**

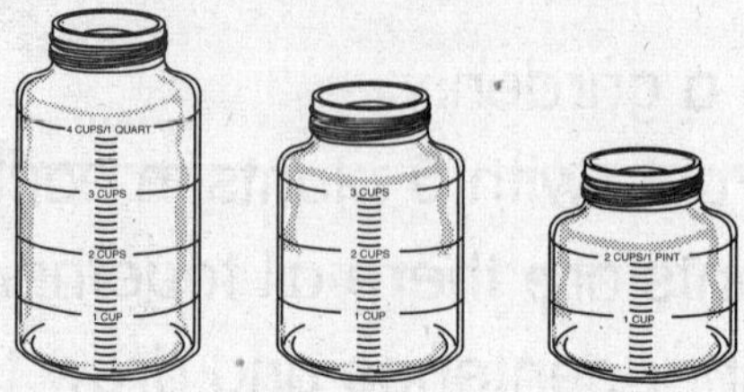

| | You Need | You Have | Enough? |
|---|---|---|---|
| **1.** | 1 quart of juice | 3 cups | |
| **2.** | 1 pint of soda | 2 cups | |
| **3.** | 1 quart of ice cream | 2 pints | |

**Make change from $1.00.**

**4.** You spend 63¢.

_______¢

**5.** You spend $0.75.

$_______

**Choose the best tool. Match.**

**6.**

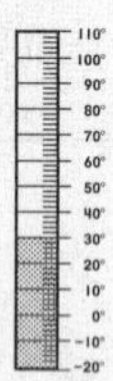

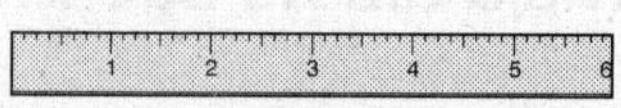


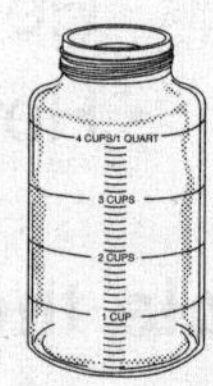

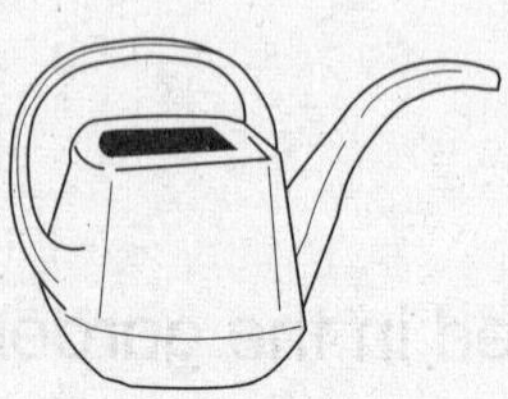